PEARSON ALWAYS LEARNING

Laboratory Experiments for Chemistry
The Central Science

Custom Edition for HCC CHEM 1412

Taken from:
Laboratory Experiments for Chemistry: The Central Science,
Fourteenth Edition
by John H. Nelson, Kenneth C. Kemp, and Michael Lufaso

Laboratory Manual for General, Organic, and Biological Chemistry,
Third Edition
by Timberlake

Chemistry: The Central Science, Fourteenth Edition
by Theodore L. Brown, H. Eugene LeMary, Jr., Bruce E. Bursten,
Catherine J. Murphy, Patrick M. Woodward, Matthew W. Stoltzfus,
and Michael W. Lufaso

Cover Art: Courtesy of Corbis.

Taken from:

Laboratory Experiments for Chemistry: The Central Science, Fourteenth Edition
by John H. Nelson, Kenneth C. Kemp, and Michael Lufaso
Copyright © 2018, 2015, 2012 by Pearson Education, Inc.
New York, NY 10013

Laboratory Manual for General, Organic, and Biological Chemistry, Third Edition
by Timberlake
Copyright © 2014, 2011, 2007, 2002 by Pearson Education, Inc.
New York, NY 10013

Chemistry: The Central Science, Fourteenth Edition
by Theodore L. Brown, H. Eugene LeMary, Jr., Bruce E. Bursten, Catherine J. Murphy,
Patrick M. Woodward, Matthew W. Stoltzfus, and Michael W. Lufaso
Copyright © 2018, 2015, 2012 by Pearson Education, Inc.
New York, NY 10013

This special edition published in cooperation with Pearson Education, Inc.

All trademarks, service marks, registered trademarks, and registered service marks are the
property of their respective owners and are used herein for identification purposes only.

Pearson Education, Inc., 330 Hudson Street, New York, New York 10013
A Pearson Education Company
www.pearsoned.com

Printed in the United States of America

1 2019

000200010272225555

ES

PEARSON   ISBN 10: 0-136-68827-6
               ISBN 13: 978-0-136-68827-3

Contents

Experiments 1–10 are taken from *Laboratory Experiments for Chemistry: The Central Science*, Fourteenth Edition by John H. Nelson, Kenneth C. Kemp, and Michael Lufaso

Experiment 11 taken from *Laboratory Manual for General, Organic, and Biological Chemistry*, Third Edition by Timberlake

List of Elements with Their Symbols and Atomic Weights

Element	Symbol	Atomic Number	Atomic Weight
Actinium	Ac	89	227.03a
Aluminum	Al	13	26.981538
Americium	Am	95	243.06a
Antimony	Sb	51	121.760
Argon	Ar	18	39.948
Arsenic	As	33	74.92160
Astatine	At	85	209.99a
Barium	Ba	56	137.327
Berkelium	Bk	97	247.07a
Beryllium	Be	4	9.012183
Bismuth	Bi	83	208.98038
Bohrium	Bh	107	270.1a
Boron	B	5	10.81
Bromine	Br	35	79.904
Cadmium	Cd	48	112.414
Calcium	Ca	20	40.078
Californium	Cf	98	251.08a
Carbon	C	6	12.0107
Cerium	Ce	58	140.116
Cesium	Cs	55	132.905452
Chlorine	Cl	17	35.453
Chromium	Cr	24	51.9961
Cobalt	Co	27	58.933194
Copernicium	Cn	112	285.2a
Copper	Cu	29	63.546
Curium	Cm	96	247.07a
Darmstadtium	Ds	110	281.2a
Dubnium	Db	105	268.1a
Dysprosium	Dy	66	162.50
Einsteinium	Es	99	252.08a
Erbium	Er	68	167.259
Europium	Eu	63	151.964
Fermium	Fm	100	257.10a
Flerovium	Fl	114	289.2a
Fluorine	F	9	18.9984016
Francium	Fr	87	223.02a
Gadolinium	Gd	64	157.25
Gallium	Ga	31	69.723
Germanium	Ge	32	72.64
Gold	Au	79	196.966569
Hafnium	Hf	72	178.49
Hassium	Hs	108	269.1a
Helium	He	2	4.002602a
Holmium	Ho	67	164.93033
Hydrogen	H	1	1.00794
Indium	In	49	114.818
Iodine	I	53	126.90447
Iridium	Ir	77	192.217
Iron	Fe	26	55.845
Krypton	Kr	36	83.80
Lanthanum	La	57	138.9055
Lawrencium	Lr	103	262.11a
Lead	Pb	82	207.2
Lithium	Li	3	6.941
Livermorium	Lv	116	293a
Lutetium	Lu	71	174.967
Magnesium	Mg	12	24.3050
Manganese	Mn	25	54.938044
Meitnerium	Mt	109	278.2a
Mendelevium	Md	101	258.10a
Mercury	Hg	80	200.59
Molybdenum	Mo	42	95.95
Moscovium	Mc	115	289.2a
Neodymium	Nd	60	144.24
Neon	Ne	10	20.1797
Neptunium	Np	93	237.05a
Nickel	Ni	28	58.6934
Nihonium	Nh	113	286.2a
Niobium	Nb	41	92.90637
Nitrogen	N	7	14.0067
Nobelium	No	102	259.10a
Oganesson	Og	118	294.2a
Osmium	Os	76	190.23
Oxygen	O	8	15.9994
Palladium	Pd	46	106.42
Phosphorus	P	15	30.973762
Platinum	Pt	78	195.078
Plutonium	Pu	94	244.06a
Polonium	Po	84	208.98a
Potassium	K	19	39.0983
Praseodymium	Pr	59	140.90766
Promethium	Pm	61	145a
Protactinium	Pa	91	231.03588
Radium	Ra	88	226.03a
Radon	Rn	86	222.02a
Rhenium	Re	75	186.207a
Rhodium	Rh	45	102.90550
Roentgenium	Rg	111	282.2a
Rubidium	Rb	37	85.4678
Ruthenium	Ru	44	101.07
Rutherfordium	Rf	104	267.1a
Samarium	Sm	62	150.36
Scandium	Sc	21	44.955908
Seaborgium	Sg	106	269.1a
Selenium	Se	34	78.97
Silicon	Si	14	28.0855
Silver	Ag	47	107.8682
Sodium	Na	11	22.989770
Strontium	Sr	38	87.62
Sulfur	S	16	32.065
Tantalum	Ta	73	180.9479
Technetium	Tc	43	98a
Tellurium	Te	52	127.60
Tennessine	Ts	117	293.2a
Terbium	Tb	65	158.92534
Thallium	Tl	81	204.3833
Thorium	Th	90	232.0377
Thulium	Tm	69	168.93422
Tin	Sn	50	118.710
Titanium	Ti	22	47.867
Tungsten	W	74	183.84
Uranium	U	92	238.02891
Vanadium	V	23	50.9415
Xenon	Xe	54	131.293
Ytterbium	Yb	70	173.04
Yttrium	Y	39	88.90584
Zinc	Zn	30	65.39
Zirconium	Zr	40	91.224

aMass of longest-lived or most important isotope.

To the Student

You are about to engage in what, for most of you, will be a unique experience. You will be collecting experimental data on your own and using your reasoning powers to draw logical conclusions about the meaning of these data. Your laboratory periods are short, and in most instances, there will not be enough time to come to the laboratory unaware of what you are to do, collect your experimental data, make conclusions and/or calculations regarding them, clean up, and hand in your results. Thus, you should *read the experimental procedure in advance* so that you can work in the lab most efficiently.

After you've read through the experiment, try to answer the prelab questions we've included at the end of each experiment. These questions will help you to understand the experiment, learn how to do the calculations required to treat your data, and give you another reason to read over the experiment in advance. You can check most of your own answers against the answers we've included in Appendix K. Also try to answer the Give It Some Thought questions that we have added to aid you in understanding the principals exemplified by the experiment.

Some of your experiments will also contain an element of *danger*. For this and other reasons, there are laboratory instructors present to assist you. They are your friends. Treat them well, and above all, don't be afraid to ask them questions. Within reason, they will be glad to help you.

Chemistry is an experimental science. The knowledge that has been accumulated through previous experiments provides the basis for today's chemistry courses. The information now being gathered will form the basis of future courses. There are basically two types of experiments that chemists conduct:

1. Qualitative—noting observations such as color, color changes, hardness, whether heat is liberated or absorbed, and odor.
2. Quantitative—noting the amount of a measurable change in mass, volume, or temperature, for example, for which the qualitative data are already known.

This laboratory manual includes both qualitative and quantitative analyses. The former determines what substances are present, and the latter determines the amounts of the substances.

It is much easier to appreciate and comprehend the science of chemistry if you actually participate in experimentation. Although there are many descriptions of the scientific method, the reasoning process involved is difficult to appreciate without performing experiments. Invariably there are experimental difficulties encountered in the laboratory that require care and patience to overcome. There are four objectives for you, the student, in the laboratory:

1. To develop the skills necessary to obtain and evaluate a reliable original result.
2. To record your results for future use.
3. To be able to draw conclusions regarding your results (with the aid of some coaching and reading in the beginning).
4. To learn to communicate your results critically and knowledgeably.

By attentively reading over the experiments in advance, and by carefully following directions and working safely in the laboratory, you will be able to accomplish all these objectives. Good luck and best wishes for an error-free and accident-free term.

Laboratory Safety and Work Instructions

Attention Student! Read the following carefully because your instructor may give you a quiz on this material.

The laboratory can be—but is not necessarily—a dangerous place. When intelligent precautions and a proper understanding of techniques are employed, the laboratory is no more dangerous than any other classroom. Most of the precautions are just common-sense practices. These include the following:

LABORATORY SAFETY

1. Wear *approved* eye protection (including splash guards) at all times while in the laboratory. (*No one will be admitted without it.*) Your safety eye protection may be slightly different from that shown, but it must include shatterproof lenses and side shields to provide protection from splashes.

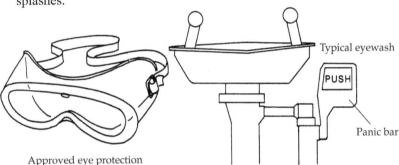

Approved eye protection

Typical eyewash

PUSH

Panic bar

The laboratory has an eyewash fountain available for your use. In the event that a chemical splashes near your eyes, you should use the fountain **before the material runs behind your eyeglasses and into your eyes.** The eyewash has a "panic bar," which enables its easy activation in an emergency.

2. Wear shoes at all times. (*No one will be admitted without them.*)
3. Eating, drinking, and smoking are strictly prohibited in the laboratory at all times.
4. Know where to find and how to use all safety and first-aid equipment (see the first page of this book).
5. Consider all chemicals to be hazardous unless you are instructed otherwise. **Dispose of chemicals as directed by your instructor.** Follow the explicit instructions given in the experiments.

6. If chemicals come into contact with your skin or eyes, wash immediately with copious amounts of water and then consult your laboratory instructor.

7. Never taste anything. Never directly smell the source of any vapor or gas. Instead, by means of your cupped hand, bring a small sample to your nose. Chemicals are not to be used to obtain a "high" or clear your sinuses.

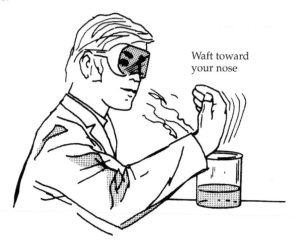

Waft toward your nose

8. Perform in the fume exhaust hood any reactions involving skin-irritating or dangerous chemicals, or unpleasant odors. This is a typical fume exhaust hood. Exhaust hoods have fans to exhaust fumes out of the hood

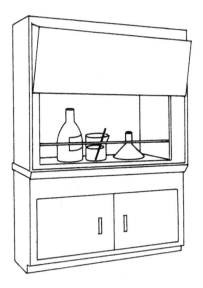

and away from the user. The hood should be used when you are studying noxious, hazardous, and flammable materials. It also has a shatterproof glass window, which may be used as a shield to protect you from minor explosions. Reagents that evolve toxic fumes are stored in the hood. Return these reagents to the hood after their use.

9. Never point a test tube that you are heating at yourself or your neighbor—it may erupt like a geyser.

10. Do not perform *any* unauthorized experiments.

11. Clean up all broken glassware *immediately*.

12. Always pour acids into water, not water into acid, because the heat of solution will cause the water to boil and the acid to spatter. "Do as you oughter, pour acid into water."

13. Avoid rubbing your eyes unless you *know* that your hands are clean.

14. When inserting glass tubing or thermometers into stoppers, *lubricate the tubing and the hole in the stopper with glycerol or water.* Wrap the rod in a towel and grasp it as close to the end being inserted as possible. Slide the glass into the rubber stopper with a twisting motion. Do not push. Finally, remove the excess lubricant by wiping with a towel. Keep your hands as close together as possible in order to reduce leverage.

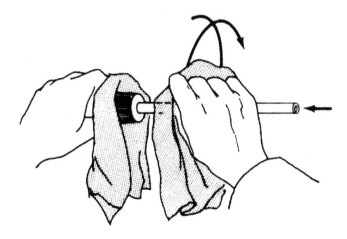

15. For safety purposes, always place the ring stand as far back on the laboratory bench as comfortable, with the long edges of the base perpendicular to the front of the bench.

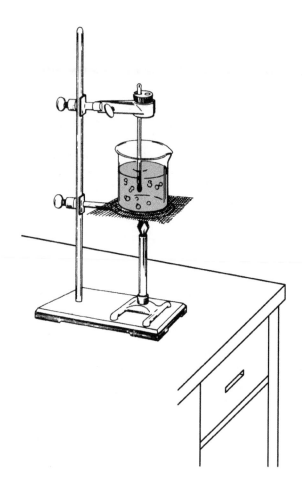

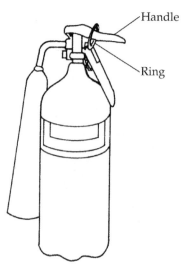

Handle

Ring

16. NOTIFY THE INSTRUCTOR IMMEDIATELY IN CASE OF AN ACCIDENT.

17. Many common reagents—for example, alcohols, acetone, and especially ether—are highly flammable. *Do not use them anywhere near open flames.*

18. Observe all special precautions mentioned in experiments.

19. Learn the location and operation of fire-protection devices.

In the unlikely event that a large chemical fire occurs, carbon dioxide fire extinguishers are available in the lab (usually mounted near one of the exits in the room). A typical carbon dioxide fire extinguisher is shown on the previous page.

In order to activate the extinguisher, you must pull the metal safety ring from the handle and then depress the handle. Direct the output from the extinguisher at the base of the flames. The carbon dioxide smothers the flames and cools the flammable material quickly. If you use the fire extinguisher, be sure to turn the extinguisher in at the stockroom so that it can be refilled immediately. If the carbon dioxide extinguisher does not extinguish the fire, evacuate the laboratory immediately and call the fire department.

One of the most frightening and potentially most serious accidents is the ignition of one's clothing. Certain types of clothing are hazardous in the laboratory and must *not* be worn. Since *sleeves* are most likely to come closest to flames, ANY CLOTHING THAT HAS BULKY OR LOOSE SLEEVES SHOULD NOT BE WORN IN THE LABORATORY. Ideally, students should wear laboratory coats with tightly fitting sleeves. Long hair also presents a hazard and must be tied back.

If a student's clothing or hair catches fire, his or her neighbors should take prompt action to prevent severe burns. Most laboratories have a water shower for such emergencies. A typical laboratory emergency water shower has the following appearance:

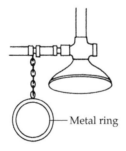

In case someone's clothing or hair is on fire, immediately lead the person to the shower and pull the metal ring. Safety showers generally dump 40 to 50 gallons of water, which should extinguish the flames. These showers generally cannot be shut off once the metal ring has been pulled. Therefore, the shower cannot be demonstrated. (Showers are checked for proper operation on a regular basis, however.)

20. Whenever possible, use hot plates in place of Bunsen burners.

BASIC INSTRUCTIONS FOR LABORATORY WORK

1. Read the assignment *before* coming to the laboratory.
2. Work independently unless instructed to do otherwise.
3. Record your results directly onto your report sheet or notebook. DO NOT RECOPY FROM ANOTHER PIECE OF PAPER.
4. Work conscientiously to avoid accidents.
5. Dispose of excess reagents as instructed by your instructor. NEVER RETURN REAGENTS TO THE REAGENT BOTTLE.
6. Do not place reagent-bottle stoppers on the desk; hold them in your hand. Your laboratory instructor will show you how to do this. Replace the stopper on the same bottle, never on a different one.
7. Leave reagent bottles on the shelf where you found them.
8. Use only the amount of reagent called for avoid excesses.
9. Whenever instructed to use water in these experiments, use distilled water unless instructed to do otherwise.
10. Keep your area clean.
11. Do not borrow apparatus from other desks. If you need extra equipment, obtain it from the stockroom.
12. When weighing, do not place chemicals directly on the balance.
13. Do not weigh hot or warm objects. Objects should be at room temperature.
14. Do not put hot objects on the desktop. Place them on a wire gauze or heat-resistant pad.

"I have read and understand these instructions as well as the laboratory safety and work instructions"

_____   _____

Student Signature   Date

COMMON LABORATORY APPARATUS

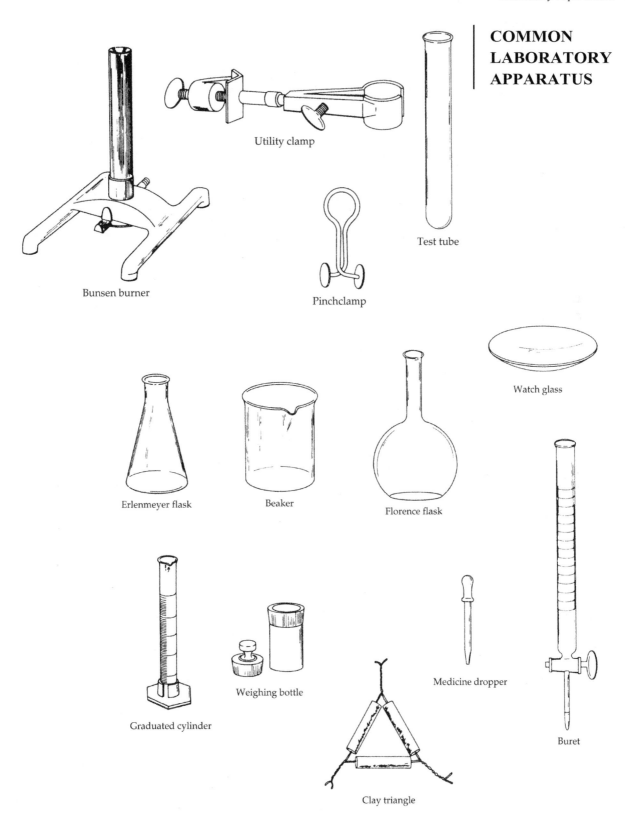

Utility clamp

Test tube

Bunsen burner

Pinchclamp

Watch glass

Erlenmeyer flask

Beaker

Florence flask

Graduated cylinder

Weighing bottle

Medicine dropper

Buret

Clay triangle

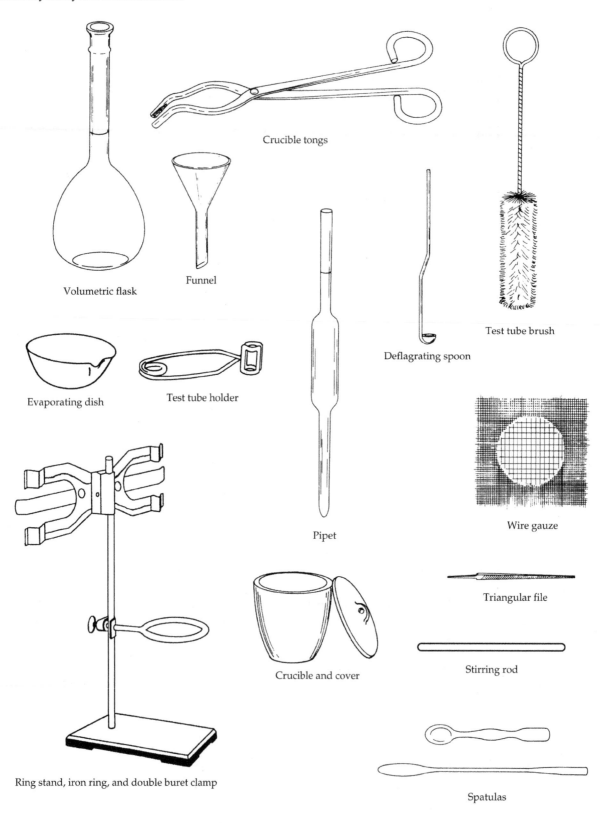

Crucible tongs

Volumetric flask

Funnel

Test tube brush

Deflagrating spoon

Evaporating dish

Test tube holder

Pipet

Wire gauze

Triangular file

Stirring rod

Crucible and cover

Ring stand, iron ring, and double buret clamp

Spatulas

Molarity, Dilutions, and Preparing Solutions

To become familiar with molarity and the methods of preparing solutions.

Apparatus

spectrophotometer and plastic cuvettes	analytical balance, capable of
100-mL volumetric flask, with cap	massing a minimum of 100 g
50-mL volumetric flask, with caps (4)	top-loading balance
25-mL volumetric flask, with caps (2)	500-mL beaker
10-mL volumetric flask	weigh boat
volumetric pipets (5 mL, 10 mL,	spatula
15 mL, 20 mL)	plastic funnel
pipet bulb	label tape

Chemicals

copper(II) sulfate   anhydrous

A *solution* is a homogeneous mixture of two or more substances. A solution is composed of a *solute* and a *solvent*. The solute is a dissolved solid, liquid, or gas. The solvent, which dissolves the solute, may also be a solid, liquid, or gas. For much of the field of chemistry, the solvent is often a liquid. Water is a common liquid solvent and will be used in this experiment to form *aqueous solutions*.

The solvent is present in a greater amount than the solute. The term *concentration* is used to designate the quantity of solute dissolved in a certain amount of solvent or solution. A solution with a greater amount of solute in a specific amount of solvent has a larger concentration than a solution with a smaller amount of solute in a specific amount of solvent. There are several ways to quantitatively express concentrations of solutions. The term *molarity* (symbol *M*) expresses the concentration as the number of moles of solute per liter of solution, as shown in equation [1].

$$Molarity = \frac{\text{moles of solute(mol)}}{\text{volume of solution(L)}} \qquad [1]$$

A 0.50 molar solution has 0.50 mole of solute per liter of solution.

GIVE IT SOME THOUGHT

If the temperature of the solution is raised and the volume of the solution increases, what happens to the molarity of the solution?

EXAMPLE 1.1

Calculate the molarity of a solution prepared by dissolving 12.2 g of barium chloride ($BaCl_2$) in enough water to form a 150.0-mL solution.

SOLUTION: The solute is barium chloride and the mass is given. The moles of $BaCl_2$ can be calculated. The volume of the solution is given in milliliters, which needs to be converted to liters.

The molar mass of $BaCl_2$ is $137.33 + (2 \times 35.453) = 208.236$ g/mol.

The moles of $BaCl_2$ is obtained by dividing the mass by the molar mass:

$$12.2 \text{ g BaCl}_2 \times \frac{1 \text{ mol BaCl}_2}{208.232 \text{ g BaCl}_2} = 0.0586 \text{ mol BaCl}_2$$

The volume of the solution is converted to liters:

$$150 \text{ mL} \times \frac{1 \text{ L}}{1000 \text{ mL}} = 0.150 \text{ L}$$

The molarity is calculated as follows:

$$\frac{0.0586 \text{ mol BaCl}_2}{0.150 \text{ L solution}} = 0.391 M$$

The concentration of a solution may be changed by changing the volume of the solution. If an aqueous solution of sodium chloride were left open to the air and some water evaporated, then it would become more concentrated. If water were added to the solution, then it would become less concentrated. The process of adding additional solvent to a solution is called *dilution*. Adding or removing solvent does not change the amount of the solute in the solution. The moles (mol) of solute before dilution equals the moles of solute after dilution. Given M = moles/volume (V) of solution, moles = $M \times V$. Considering a concentrated and a diluted solution, $mol_{conc} = mol_{dil}$. Then Equation [2], which is known as a *dilution equation*, may be derived by substitution.

$$M_{conc}V_{conc} = M_{dil}V_{dil} \qquad\qquad [2]$$

EXAMPLE 1.2

How many milliliters of 8.0 M HCl are needed to make 250 mL of 0.25 M HCl?

SOLUTION: The more concentrated solution is diluted to form a less concentrated solution. The concentration of the more concentrated solution is known, and the concentration and volume of the more dilute solution are given. Three of the four variables in the equation $M_{conc}V_{conc} = M_{dil}V_{dil}$ are therefore known. Calculate the volume of the more concentrated solution needed to prepare the more dilute solution.

Rearrange the equation to solve for $V_{conc} = \dfrac{M_{dil}V_{dil}}{M_{conc}}$.

$$M_{dil} = 0.25M, V_{dil} = 250 \text{ mL}, M_{conc} = 8.0M$$

$$V_{conc} = \frac{M_{dil}V_{dil}}{M_{conc}} = \frac{(0.25M)(250 \text{ mL})}{(8.0M)} = 7.8 \text{ mL}$$

Use the dilution equation cautiously, since it works only for dilutions and should not be used for calculations that involve mixing two or more solutions or for any type of titration or chemical reaction.

The preparation of low-concentration and/or low-volume solutions may be challenging because of the difficulty of accurately obtaining a small amount of a solute. Consider the following example and preparation of a low-concentration solution.

EXAMPLE 1.3

Cisplatin is a drug for treatment of cancer with the chemical formula $Pt(NH_3)_2Cl_2$. The maximum concentration is reported as 0.5 mg/mL. Convert this concentration to molarity. Calculate the amount of $Pt(NH_3)_2Cl_2$ in grams that is needed to make a 10.0-mL solution at that maximum concentration.

SOLUTION: The molar mass of $Pt(NH_3)_2Cl_2$ is $195.08 + (2 \times 14.007) + (6 \times 1.0079) + (2 \times 35.453) = 300.047$ g/mol.

The desired concentration is 0.5 mg/mL, or 0.5 mg per 1 mL.

Convert the concentration to units of molarity. First, convert from milligrams to moles of $Pt(NH_3)_2Cl_2$:

$$0.5 \text{ mg Pt(NH}_3)_2\text{Cl}_2 \times \frac{1 \times 10^{-3} \text{ g}}{1 \text{ mg}} \times \frac{1 \text{ mol}}{300.047 \text{ g}} = 1.67 \times 10^{-6} \text{ mol Pt(NH}_3)_2\text{Cl}_2$$

The volume is given in milliliters, so convert to liters.

$$1.00 \text{ mL} \times \frac{1 \times 10^{-3} \text{ L}}{1 \text{ mL}} = 0.00100 \text{ L}$$

The molarity is

$$M = \frac{1.67 \times 10^{-6} \text{ mol}}{0.00100 \text{ L}} = 0.00167 \ M$$

Next, find the amount of $Pt(NH_3)_2Cl_2$ needed to prepare a 10.0-mL solution with a concentration of 0.00167 M. The volume of the solution is $(10.0 \text{ mL}) \times (1 \times 10^{-3} \text{ L/1 mL}) = 0.0100$ L.

Rearranging the molarity equation yields $M = \text{mol}/V$, so

$$\text{mol} = M \times V = (0.00167 \ M) \times (0.0100 \text{ L}) = 1.67 \times 10^{-5} \text{ mol Pt(NH}_3)_2\text{Cl}_2$$

Determine the mass from the moles of $Pt(NH_3)_2Cl_2$ using the molar mass.

$$1.67 \times 10^{-5} \text{ mol Pt(NH}_3)_2\text{Cl}_2 \times \frac{300.047 \text{ g Pt(NH}_3)_2\text{Cl}_2}{1 \text{ mol Pt(NH}_3)_2\text{Cl}_2} = 0.0050 \text{ g Pt(NH}_3)_2\text{Cl}_2$$

Accurately obtaining small amounts of reagents can be difficult. For this reason, it is easier to prepare a solution of higher concentration and then perform multiple dilutions. This is known as *serial dilution*.

EXAMPLE 1.4

A stock solution "S" is prepared by obtaining 0.125 g $Pt(NH_3)_2Cl_2$ and dissolving to form a 10.00-mL solution. Another solution ("A") is prepared by taking 2.00 mL of the stock solution and diluting to form a 10.00-mL solution. Another solution ("B") is prepared by taking 2.00 mL of solution "A" and dissolving to form a 10.00-mL solution. A schematic of the serial dilution is shown in Figure 1.1. Determine the concentration of $Pt(NH_3)_2Cl_2$ in the "B" solution.

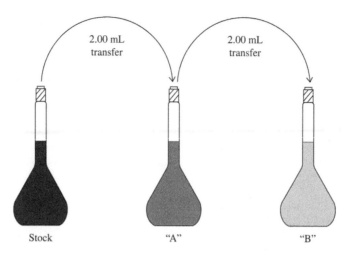

▲FIGURE 1.1 Serial dilution. A quantitative portion of the more concentrated solution is transferred and diluted with the solvent to make a solution of lower concentration.

SOLUTION: The molar mass of $Pt(NH_3)_2Cl_2$ is

$$195.08 + (2 \times 14.007) + (6 \times 1.0079) + (2 \times 35.453) = 300.047 \text{ g/mol}$$

Determine the moles of $Pt(NH_3)_2Cl_2$ from the mass:

$$0.125 \text{ g } Pt(NH_3)_2Cl_2 \times \frac{1 \text{ mol}}{300.047 \text{ g}} = 0.000417 \text{ mol}$$

Calculate the molarity of the stock solution. The volume is

$$10.00 \text{ mL} \times \frac{1 \times 10^{-3} \text{ L}}{1 \text{ mL}} = 0.01000 \text{ L}$$

The molarity of the stock solution is

$$M = \frac{\text{mol}/V = 0.000417 \text{ mol}}{0.01000 \text{ L}} = 0.0417 \text{ } M$$

Calculate the molarity of solution "A." It is being prepared using the stock solution and diluting. $M_{conc}V_{conc} = M_{dil}V_{dil}$, so solve for M_{dil}.

$$M_{dil} = \frac{M_{conc}V_{conc}}{V_{dil}} = 0.0417 \text{ } M \times \frac{2.00 \text{ mL}}{10.00 \text{ mL}} = 0.00833 \text{ } M$$

Calculate the molarity of solution "B." It is being prepared by using solution "A" and diluting.

For this dilution, M_{conc} is the concentration of the "A" solution.

$$M_{dil} = \frac{M_{conc}V_{conc}}{V_{dil}} = 0.00833 \text{ } M \times \frac{2.00 \text{ mL}}{10.00 \text{ mL}} = 0.00167 \text{ } M$$

The concentration solution "B" is 0.00167 M, the same as that found in Example 1.3. It is much easier to accurately obtain 0.125 g of $Pt(NH_3)_2Cl_2$ and perform serial dilutions than to try to accurately obtain 0.0050 g and prepare a single low-concentration solution.

There are several methods to measure the concentration of a solution. One method relies on the fact that solutions of some compounds absorb light. A solution with a larger concentration absorbs more light than a solution with a smaller concentration. The relationship between the absorbance of a solution and its concentration is given by Beer's Law, equation [3], where A is the *absorbance* of the solution (unitless), ε is the molar absorptivity constant ($L\ mol^{-1}cm^{-1}$), b is the path length the light travels through the sample (cm^{-1}), and c is the molar concentration of the solution ($mol\ L^{-1}$).

$$A = \varepsilon bc \qquad [3]$$

The absorbance of a solution is directly proportional to its concentration. The molar absorptivity constant is a property inherent in a given chemical compound.

The absorbance of a solution may be experimentally measured using a spectrophotometer, which measures the quantity of light that passes through a solution. The *percent transmission* (%T) is the amount of light transmitted; at 100% T no light is absorbed, and at 0% all of the light is absorbed. The relationship between absorbance and percent transmission is given in Equation [4].

$$A = 2 - \log(\%T) \qquad [4]$$

EXAMPLE 1.5

The percent transmission of a solution is determined to be 23.5%. Calculate the absorbance of the solution.

SOLUTION: The relationship between absorbance and percent transmission is $A = 2 - \log(\%T)$.

$$A = 2 - \log(\%T) = A = 2 - \log(23.5) = 0.629$$

Using a spectrophotometer involves placing the solution in a transparent plastic or glass cuvette. The light source is a tungsten lamp that emits white light. A specific wavelength can be selected using optics of the spectrophotometer. The wavelength is generally chosen at the wavelength of maximum absorption for the solution.

A standard curve can be made by making a series of solutions of known concentration and preparing a graph of absorbance versus molarity. The slope of this line may be used to determine the concentration of an unknown solution from its absorbance.

EXAMPLE 1.6

A series of $NiCl_2$ solutions were prepared at different concentrations, and their percent transmissions were measured, as shown in the following table. A 1-cm-path-length cuvette was used to contain the solution. The percent transmission of a solution of $NiCl_2$ with an unknown concentration was 22.7%. Determine the concentration of the unknown $NiCl_2$ solution.

	"A"	"B"	"C"	"D"	Unknown
Molarity, M	0.0330	0.0206	0.0070	0.0023	–
Percent transmission, %T	16.3	33.3	68.5	88.1	22.7

SOLUTION: Calculate the absorbance of each, using the equation $A = 2 - \log(\%T)$.

Calculation for solution "A": $A = 2 - \log(16.3) = 0.788$

The absorbance values are shown in the following table.

	"A"	"B"	"C"	"D"	Unknown
Absorbance	0.788	0.477	0.164	0.0549	0.644

Plot absorbance versus concentration for the solutions of known concentration, and include the trend line equation.

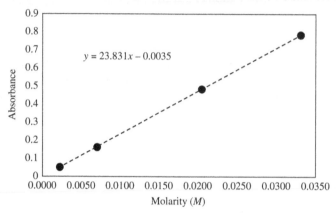

The slope of the line divided by the path length (1 cm^{-1}) is the molar absorptivity, $\varepsilon = 23.83 \, M^{-1} \, \text{cm}^{-1}$.

Solve $A = \varepsilon bc$ for concentration.

$$c = \frac{A}{\varepsilon b} = \frac{0.644}{23.83 \, M^{-1} \, \text{cm}^{-1} \times 1 \text{ cm}} = 0.0270 \, M$$

To check this result, note that this concentration is between the concentrations of solutions A and B.

PROCEDURE | A. Preparing a Stock Solution of Known Concentration

Prior to preparing the stock solution, turn on the spectrophotometer so it may warm up. Obtain approximately 4 g of $CuSO_4$ using a top-loading balance. Obtain a clean and dry 100-mL volumetric flask and determine the mass of the empty volumetric flask. Add the $CuSO_4$ to the flask with the aid of a funnel. Determine the mass of the volumetric flask and $CuSO_4$. Add approximately 75 mL deionized (DI) H_2O to the flask, and swirl to dissolve the $CuSO_4$. Depending on the size of the crystals of $CuSO_4$, it may take several minutes to fully dissolve. When all of the crystals have dissolved, finish filling the volumetric flask to the calibration mark. The use of a plastic transfer pipet or dropper makes dropwise control possible near the mark. Add a cap to the flask, and invert and swirl several times to ensure the solution is entirely mixed. Label the stock solution as "S." The concentration of the stock solution may be calculated from the moles of the copper sulfate and the volume of the solution. Calculate the molarity of the stock solution.

B. Preparing the Spectrophotometer for use

Adjust the wavelength setting to 625 nm on the spectrophotometer, which is the analytical wavelength and the wavelength of maximum absorption for $CuSO_4$. Obtain a plastic cuvette and, using a marker, make a small mark on the top of the cuvette. This will aid in inserting the cuvette into the spectrophotometer in the same orientation for each measurement. Fill the cuvette with DI H_2O until it is about 80% full, and then insert it into the sample holder of the spectrophotometer. Adjust the spectrophotometer to 100.0% transmission; for some models this may be done with the push of a button.

C. Measuring the Absorbance of the Stock Solution

Empty the DI H_2O from the cuvette. The cuvette probably has residual water on the walls or bottom of the cuvette, so the cuvette should be rinsed several times with several small portions of the stock solution. Fill the cuvette with the stock $CuSO_4$ until it is about 80% full, and then insert it into the sample holder of the spectrophotometer, using the same orientations as before. Record the percent transmission. Calculate the absorbance of the stock solution of $CuSO_4$ using Equation [4]. Remove the cuvette and empty the contents into a waste beaker.

D. Preparing Volumetric Pipets for use

For the preparation of solutions with an accurate concentration, the highest-quality results are obtained when clean and accurate glassware is used. Glassware such as a beaker or Erlenmeyer flask is not typically used, because those are less accurate than a volumetric flask and volumetric pipet. The volumetric glassware has a mark around the circumference to indicate the fill point. For aqueous solutions, the bottom of the meniscus should be level with the mark. Before use, the pipet should be washed with soapy water and rinsed with DI H_2O. Use the pipet bulb to blow out any of the rinse water, and wipe the pipet tip dry. There might be some residual water inside the pipet, which would dilute the solution slightly. Into a clean beaker, pour a small amount of the solution that is to be transferred by pipet. Immerse the tip of the pipet in the solution, and fill the pipet about 10% full. Remove the pipet bulb and quickly place your finger over the top of the pipet. Dry the pipet tip, move the pipet to a horizontal position, and then rotate the pipet to allow the inside of the pipet to be coated by the solution. Return the pipet to a vertical orientation, and allow the solution to drain into a waste beaker. The inside of the pipet is now wetted with the solution to be transferred and is ready for use.

E. Construction of a Calibration Graph

A plot of absorbance (A) versus molarity (M) will be prepared to construct a calibration graph. A total of five solutions will be used, the stock solution and four dilutions, as data points. Obtain and clean four 50-mL volumetric flasks, and individually label each (A, B, C, D). Using the appropriate pre-rinsed pipets and stock solution, add 5.00 mL to volumetric flask A, 10.00 mL to volumetric flask B, 15.00 mL to volumetric flask C, and 20.00 mL to volumetric flask D. Dilute each flask to the calibration mark using DI H_2O. Cover with a cap, and then mix each thoroughly by inverting and swirling for a minute or so. If you are sharing a spectrophotometer, be sure to re-zero the instrument with DI H_2O in your cuvette before each use. Rinse the cuvette with solution D, and then measure and record the percent transmission. Repeat this for solutions C, D, and A. Calculate the molarity of each solution. Calculate the absorbance of each solution using Equation [4]. After the laboratory session, prepare a plot of absorbance (A) versus molarity (M) using the five data points. Include the trend line equation for a linear fit.

GIVE IT SOME THOUGHT

Does the "lightest" or the "darkest" solution have the highest percent transmission? The highest absorbance?

F. Serial Dilution Preparation of a Solution of Lower Concentration

A serial dilution will be done by using the stock solution and performing two dilutions to obtain a solution of lower concentration. Label two cleaned 25.00-mL volumetric flasks (X and Y). To a 25.00-mL volumetric flask "X" add 10.00 mL of the stock solution, using the appropriate pipet. Dilute to the calibration mark with DI H_2O and then cover. Swirl and invert to ensure thorough mixing. Pipet 10.00 mL of the solution in "X" to volumetric flask "Y." Dilute to the calibration mark with DI H_2O and then cover. Swirl and invert to ensure thorough mixing. Measure the percent transmission of the solution in volumetric flask "Y." Calculate the concentration of the serial-diluted sample in volumetric flask "Y." Determine the molarity of the solution using the calibration graph and the measured absorbance. Assuming the calibration graph to be the accepted value, calculate a percent error for the molarity of the solution in "Y."

G. Directly Preparing a Solution of Lower Concentration

Using an analytical balance, obtain 0.0650 g $CuSO_4$ in a small plastic weigh boat. Add it to a clean 10.00-mL volumetric flask labeled "Z." Fill with about 7 mL DI H_2O and swirl to dissolve the $CuSO_4$. When all of the $CuSO_4$ crystals have dissolved, finish filling the volumetric flask to the calibration mark. Swirl and invert to ensure thorough mixing. Measure the percent transmission of the solution in volumetric flask "Z." Calculate the concentration of the solution, using the mass of the $CuSO_4$ and the volume of the solution. Determine the molarity of the solution, using the equation obtained from the calibration graph and the absorbance calculated from the measured percent transmission. Assuming the calibration graph to be the accepted or true value, calculate a percent error for the molarity of the solution in "Z."

GIVE IT SOME THOUGHT

Why is it difficult to precisely obtain small quantities of a sample?

H. Determining the Concentration of an Unknown Solution

Obtain an unknown solution and label it with the ID given to you by your instructor (e.g., "U1"). Measure the percent transmission of the unknown solution. Determine the molarity of the solution, using the equation obtained from the calibration graph and the absorbance calculated from the measured percent transmission.

Clean and rinse all glassware thoroughly.

Waste Disposal Instructions: Dispose of all waste as indicated by your instructor.

Name _____ Desk _____

Date _____ Laboratory Instructor _____

Molarity, Dilutions, and Preparing Solutions | 1 Pre-lab Questions

Before beginning this experiment in the laboratory, you should be able to answer the following questions.

1. Sodium chloride is dissolved in water to form a solution. Identify the solute and the solvent.

2. An aqueous solution of sucrose $(C_{12}H_{22}O_{11})$ is prepared by dissolving 6.5532 g in sufficient deionized water to form a 50.00-mL solution. Calculate the molarity of the solution.

3.   An aqueous solution of iron(II) sulfate $(FeSO_4)$ is prepared by dissolving 2.85 g in sufficient deionized water to form a 25.00-mL solution. Calculate the molarity of the solution.

4.   Determine the absorbance if the percent transmission is 68.6%.

5.   A pipet is used to transfer 5.00 mL of a 1.25 M stock solution in flask "S" to a 25.00-mL volumetric flask "B," which is then diluted with DI H_2O to the calibration mark. The solution is thoroughly mixed. Next, 2.00 mL of the solution in volumetric flask "A" is transferred by pipet to a 50.00-mL volumetric flask "B" and then diluted with DI H_2O to the calibration mark. Calculate the molarity of the solution in volumetric flask "B."

REPORT SHEET | EXPERIMENT

Molarity, Dilutions, and | 1
Preparing Solutions

A. Preparing a Stock Solution of Known Concentration

1. Mass of 100-mL volumetric flask, g _____

2. Mass of 100-mL volumetric flask and $CuSO_4$, g _____

3. Mass of $CuSO_4$, g _____

4. Volume of stock solution, mL _____

5. Molarity of stock solution "S," M _____

   (Show calculations.)

B. Preparing the Spectrophotometer for use

1. Percent transmission of DI H_2O, %T _____

2. Absorbance of DI H_2O, A _____

C. Measuring the Absorbance of the Stock Solution

1. Percent transmission of stock solution, %T _____

2. Absorbance of stock solution, A _____

E. Construction of a Calibration Graph

	"A"	"B"	"C"	"D"
Volume of stock solution, mL	5.00	10.00	15.00	20.00
Volume of prepared solution, mL	50.00	50.00	50.00	50.00
Molarity, M				
Percent transmission, %T				
Absorbance, A				

F. Serial Dilution Preparation of a Solution of Lower Concentration

1. Percent transmission of solution "Y," %T _____

2. Absorbance of solution "Y," A _____

3. Molarity of solution "Y" calculated from dilutions, M _____

4. Molarity of solution "Y" determined from calibration graph, M _____

5. Percent error of molarity of solution "Y," % _____

G. Directly Preparing a Solution of Lower Concentration

1. Mass of $CuSO_4$, g _____

2. Molarity of solution "Z," M _____

3. Percent transmission of solution "Z," %T _____

4. Absorbance of solution "Z," A _____

5. Molarity of solution "Z" determined from calibration graph, M _____

6. Percent error of molarity of solution "Z," % _____

H. Unknown Solution

1. Identity label of unknown _____

2. Percent transmission of unknown solution, %T _____

3. Absorbance of unknown solution, A _____

4. Molarity of solution determined from calibration graph, M _____

QUESTIONS

1. A stock solution of potassium permanganate ($KMnO_4$) was prepared by dissolving 13.0 g $KMnO_4$ with DI H_2O in a 100.00-mL volumetric flask and diluting to the calibration mark. Determine the molarity of the solution.

2. By pipet, 15.00 mL of the stock solution of potassium permanganate ($KMnO_4$) from Question 1 was transferred to a 50.00-mL volumetric flask and diluted to the calibration mark. Determine the molarity of the resulting solution.

3. Describe how to prepare 100.00 mL of a 0.250 M sodium chloride (NaCl) solution using sodium chloride powder.

4. Describe how to prepare 50.00 mL of a 3.00 M hydrochloric acid solution using 12.0 M HCl.

Freezing Point Depression

To use the concept of freezing point depression to determine the molar mass of a compound by determination of the freezing point of a pure solvent and a solution.

Apparatus

25 × 200 mm test tube (outer)	clamp
20 × 150 mm test tube (inner)	magnetic stirring plate
two hole stopper, one side slit	top loading 0.001g balance and
thermometer, alcohol	0.0001 g analytical balance
wire stirring loop	stopwatch
800 mL beaker (×2), 250 mL	spatula
beaker (×1)	weighboat
ring stand and test tube clamp	plastic funnel, 3″

Chemicals

Lauric acid	Ice
Unknown solid assigned by	
instructor	

WORK IN GROUPS OF TWO, DEPENDING ON EQUIPMENT AVAILABILITY, BUT ANALYZE YOUR DATA INDIVIDUALLY

Solutions are homogeneous mixtures that contain two or more substances. The major component is called the *solvent*, and the minor component is called the *solute*. Because the solution is composed primarily of solvent, physical properties of a solution resemble those of the solvent. The cooling system in an automobile engine contains a mixture of primarily ethylene glycol and water. In cold climates, the low temperature freezes water into ice, yet the solution of ethylene glycol and water in the engine block and radiator doesn't freeze when exposed to the same low temperature. When a solute is dissolved into a liquid solvent, the freezing point temperature of the solution is lowered compared to that of the pure solvent due to the interactions between the solute and solvent particles. The magnitude of the freezing point depression is proportional to the number of moles, the quantity, of dissolved solute particles. It doesn't depend on the kind, identity or form of the solute particles, which could be molecules, atoms, simple monatomic ions, or polyatomic ions. The freezing point depression is a **colligative property** that depends on the collective effect of the number of solute particles (ions and/or molecules). The colligative properties include vapor pressure lowering, boiling point elevation, freezing point lowering, and osmotic pressure. Experiments have found that the dissolution of a nonvolatile

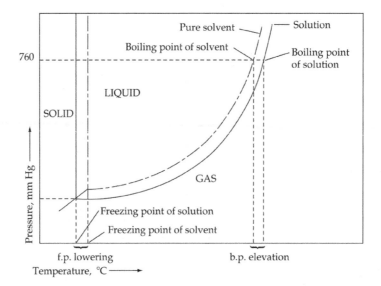

▲FIGURE 2.1 Phase diagram for a solvent and a solution.

solute (one with very low vapor pressure) in a solvent lowers the vapor pressure of the solvent, which in turn raises the boiling point and lowers the freezing point. This is shown graphically in the phase diagram provided in Figure 2.1.

The change in freezing point, ΔT_f, is directly proportional to the molal concentration (m) of solute in the solution, including the van't Hoff factor i, as follows

$$\Delta T_f = T_f(\text{solution}) - T_f(\text{solvent}) = -iK_f m$$

where K_f is the molal freezing point depression constant of the solvent, which has units of °C/m. Selected molal freezing point depression constants are given in Table 2.1. The molality (m) is represented by the number of moles of solute per 1 kg of solvent. The molality concentration unit is used because it is not temperature dependent. The van't Hoff factor for a nonelectrolyte is $i = 1$. For electrolytes, the value of i depends on how the solute ionizes in the solvent. A mole of sodium chloride forms two moles of ions in water, $NaCl \longrightarrow Na^+(aq) + Cl^-(aq)$, thus $i = 2$.

TABLE 2.1 Molal Freezing Point Constants

Solvent	Freezing Point (°C)	K_f (°C/m)
Acetic acid (CH_3COOH)	16.6	3.90
Acetone (C_3H_6O)	−94.9	4.04
Benzene (C_6H_6)	5.5	5.12
Chloroform ($CHCl_3$)	−63.5	4.68
Cyclohexane (C_6H_{12})	6.6	20.4
Ethyl alcohol (C_2H_5OH)	−114.6	1.99
Lauric acid ($C_{12}H_{24}O_2$)	43.2	3.90
Naphthalene ($C_{10}H_8$)	80.6	6.9
Phenol (C_6H_6O)	40.5	7.40
Water (H_2O)	0.0	1.86

GIVE IT SOME THOUGHT

What is the difference between molarity and molality?

EXAMPLE 2.1

Ethylene glyol, a nonelectrolyte with the chemical formula $C_2H_6O_2$, is a component of antifreeze. A cooling system in a vehicle holds 6.00 L of the antifreeze mixture with 25:75 volume ethylene glycol: water. The density of water is 1.00 g/cm³ and the density of ethylene glycol is 1.11 g/cm³. Determine the freezing point of the solution.

SOLUTION: The mixture contains 1.50 L ethylene glycol and 4.50 L water based on the given volume ratio. The molality is defined as mol solute/kg solvent. The moles of solute (ethylene glycol) are found by using the density equation to find the mass of the ethylene glycol, then find the moles of ethylene glycol.

$$\text{Mass ethylene glycol} = 1.50 \text{ L} \left(\frac{1000 \text{ mL}}{1 \text{ L}}\right)\left(\frac{1 \text{ cm}^3}{1 \text{ mL}}\right)\left(\frac{1.11 \text{ g}}{1 \text{ cm}^3}\right) = 1.67 \times 10^3 \text{ g } C_2H_6O_2$$

$$1.67 \times 10^3 \text{ g } C_2H_6O_2 \left(\frac{1 \text{ mol } C_2H_6O_2}{62.07 \text{ g } C_2H_6O_2}\right) = 26.9 \text{ mol } C_2H_6O_2$$

The mass of the solvent (water) is found by:

$$4.50 \text{ L } H_2O\left(\frac{1000 \text{ mL}}{1 \text{ L}}\right)\left(\frac{1 \text{ cm}^3}{1 \text{ mL}}\right)\left(\frac{1.00 \text{ g}}{1 \text{ cm}^3}\right)\left(\frac{1 \text{ kg}}{1000 \text{ g}}\right) = 4.50 \text{ kg } H_2O$$

The molality of the solution is:

$$\text{molality} = \left(\frac{26.9 \text{ mol } C_2H_6O_2}{4.50 \text{ kg } H_2O}\right) = 5.98 \ m$$

The freezing point depression is:

$$\Delta Tf = -iK_f m = -1(1.86 \text{ °C/m})(5.96 \text{ m}) = -11.1 \text{ °C}$$

The freezing point of pure water is 0.0 °C, thus solving $\Delta T_f = T_f(\text{solution}) - T_f(\text{solvent})$ for $T_f(\text{solution})$ gives:

$$T_f(\text{solution}) = T_f(\text{solvent}) + \Delta T_f = 0.0 \text{ °C} + (-11.1 \text{ °C}) = -11.1 \text{ °C}$$

EXAMPLE 2.2

In cold climates, salt is added to the roads to melt the ice and snow as a safety measure. A saturated solution of sodium chloride in water has a mass of 360.0 g sodium chloride per 1.00 kg of water. Determine the temperature at which the mixture will freeze.

SOLUTION: The sodium chloride is soluble in water and dissolves forming two ions in solution. The ideal van't Hoff factor (i) is 2 in this example.[*]

$$NaCl(s) \longrightarrow Na^+(aq) + Cl^-(aq)$$

---

[*]It should be noted that at high concentrations the van't Hoff factor deviates from the ideal integer value.

Determine the molality (mol/kg) of the solution. Find the moles of ions in solution.

$$moles\ NaCl = (360.0\ g)/(58.44\ g/mol) = 6.16\ mol$$

The molality of the solution is:

$$\frac{6.16\ mol\ NaCl}{1.00\ kg\ H_2O} = 6.16\ m$$

Similar to the previous example, the $\Delta T_f = -iK_f m = -2(1.86\ °C/m)(6.16\ m) = -22.9\ °C$

$$T_f(solution) = -22.9\ °C$$

EXAMPLE 2.3

Freezing point depression experiments can be used to determine the molar mass of an unknown substance. A solution is prepared by dissolving 0.100 g of a substance in 20.0 g cyclohexane. The freezing point of the solution was lowered 1.06 °C compared to pure cyclohexane. Assuming the unknown substance is a nonelectrolyte, determine the molar mass of the solute.

SOLUTION: From $\Delta T_f = -iK_f m$, the molality of the solution may be found:

$$m = \frac{\Delta T_f}{-iK_f} = \frac{-1.06\ °C}{-1 \times 20.0\ °C/m} = 0.0530\ m$$

Find the moles of solute for the solution:

$$0.0530 \frac{mol}{kg\ C_6H_{12}} = \frac{moles\ of\ substance}{20.0 \times 10^{-3}\ kg\ C_6H_{12}}$$

$$moles\ of\ substance = 0.0530 \frac{mol}{kg\ C_6H_{12}} \times 20.0 \times 10^{-3}\ kg\ C_6H_{12} = 1.06 \times 10^{-3}\ mol$$

Determine the molar mass of the solute:

$$molar\ mass = \frac{0.100\ g}{1.06 \times 10^{-3}\ mol} = 94.3\ g/mol$$

In this experiment, you will determine the molar mass of an unknown. You will do this by determining the freezing point depression of a lauric acid solution having a known added mass of your unknown. The freezing temperature is difficult to ascertain by direct visual observation because of a phenomenon called supercooling and because solidification of solutions usually occurs over a broad temperature range. Temperature-time graphs, called cooling curves, reveal freezing temperatures rather clearly.

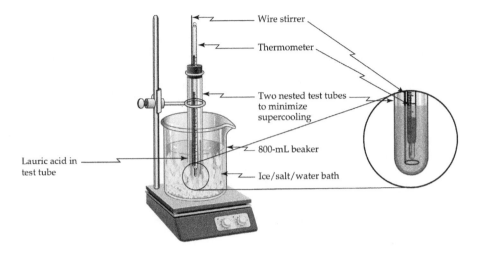

Wire stirrer

Thermometer

Two nested test tubes to minimize supercooling

800-mL beaker

Lauric acid in test tube

Ice/salt/water bath

▲FIGURE 2.2 Apparatus for determination of cooling curve.

A. Preparation of Experimental Apparatus and Freezing Point Determination of Lauric Acid

PROCEDURE

Prepare a water bath with a sufficient liquid level, about 650 mL in the 800 mL beaker, to cover the bottom one half of the test tube when it is placed into the water bath. Begin heating the beaker with the water while stirring with a stir bar. Maintain the water bath temperature near 70–80 °C and avoid boiling. Add about 300 mL of tap water and some ice cubes in a second cooling 400 mL beaker.

Construct the freezing point depression experimental apparatus similar to the one shown in Figure 2.2. Ensure the test tube, two-hole stopper, stirrer, and thermometer are clean and dry. Assemble the experimental apparatus by placing the stirrer through one hole of the stopper and the thermometer through the side slit of the stopper. Determine the mass of the freezing point depression apparatus on a top loading balance. Obtain approximately 10 g of the solid lauric acid in a weighboat, and then transfer into the inner test tube with the aid of a funnel. Insert, but don't force, the two-hole stopper with stirrer and thermometer into the test tube, and then determine the mass of the apparatus with the lauric acid.

Clamp the test tube and place it in the heated water bath, ensuring that the bottom of the test tube is not touching the beaker or stir bar. Melt all of the lauric acid and ensure that the bulb of the thermometer is below the liquid level of the lauric acid. Continue heating, with intermediate stirring, until the temperature is near 50 °C. Remove the apparatus from the water bath and clamp higher on the ring stand.

 GIVE IT SOME THOUGHT

Why is it necessary to stir the solution while cooling?

Continuously stir the lauric acid with the stirring wire loop as it cools. After it cools to 50 °C, with continuous stirring, read and record the temperature to the nearest 0.2 °C every 30 seconds for the next 5 minutes. Next, lower the beaker into the cooled water and continue to stir, if the lauric acid is not completely solid, then record the temperature every 30 seconds for at least another 8 minutes. Repeat the experiment for a second trial with the same lauric acid by heating until fully liquefied, then cooling and recording the temperatures in the same manner as the first trial.

GIVE IT SOME THOUGHT

What valuable information does a temperature-time graph give you for this experiment?

B. Freezing Point Determination of a Lauric Acid Solution

Dry the cooled apparatus from part A and determine the mass. Obtain a designation of an unknown from your lab instructor. Obtain about 1 gram of the specified unknown, then transfer to the test tube. Measure the mass of the apparatus with the lauric acid and unknown. Clamp the apparatus in the water bath and melt the mixture of the two solids. Stir the completely melted solution for several minutes to ensure adequate mixing to form a homogeneous solution. In some cases, there may be small crystals remaining after stirring the liquid solution, but even if these remain for several minutes you may continue with the cooling procedure. Remove the test tube from the hot water bath and record the temperature to the nearest 0.2 °C every 30 seconds under constant stirring. Cool in air for 5 minutes, and then cool in the cold water bath for an additional 5 minutes. Add an additional ~0.5 g, precisely determine the mass, of the same unknown. Conduct the experiment again with the lauric acid and unknown by heating until fully liquefied, then cooling and recording the temperatures in the same manner as the previous trial.

C. Waste Disposal and Cleanup

At the completion of the experiment, melt the lauric acid solution and pour into a waste container. Thoroughly clean the glassware, stir wire, and thermometer by scrubbing with a brush while washing with soap and hot water in the sink.

GIVE IT SOME THOUGHT

a. What range do you expect to see for the molar mass of your unknown?
b. Would you expect the molar mass to be 1×10^{-3} g/mol? Why or why not?
c. Would you expect the molar mass to be 1×10^{9} g/mol? Why or why not?

For each of the four freezing point determination trials of the pure solvent and solution, individually plot cooling curve graphs of the temperature (as the ordinate, vertical axis) versus time in seconds (as the abscissa, horizontal axis). The freezing point of the pure lauric acid solution may be determined by the intersection of the linear regions of the cooling portion of the liquid region and the freezing region, see Figure 2.3. It may be necessary to prepare a second graph of each with a narrower x-axis and y-axis range. Ensure the completely solid region, with a rapid temperature decrease, is not included in the freezing region that contains both liquid and solid components. Determine the average freezing point from each pure solvent experiment. Determine the freezing point from each solution trial.

Determine the ΔT_f for the solution using $T_f(\text{solution}) - T_f(\text{solvent})$. Calculate the molality of the solution using the freezing point depression constant (K_f) for lauric acid. Determine the moles of unknown solute using the freezing point depression equation and assuming the van't Hoff factor is equal to 1 for a nonelectrolyte organic compound. The mass of the solvent is the mass of the lauric acid, measured in the first trial, in units of kilograms. Calculate the experimental molar mass using the mass of the unknown organic compound added as the solute and the moles of unknown for experiments 3 and 4. Ensure correct significant figures and units are used in all calculations.

CALCULATIONS

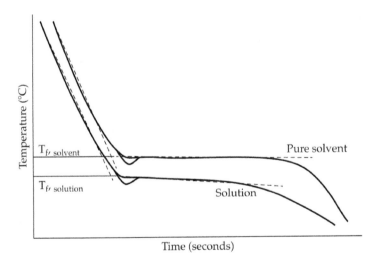

▲**FIGURE 2.3** Cooling curve for a pure solvent and solution.

Freezing Point Depression | 2 Pre-lab Questions

Before beginning this experiment in the laboratory, you should be able to answer the following questions.

1. Distinguish between solute and solvent.

2. Write the expression for the freezing point depression.

3. List three colligative properties and suggest a rationale for the choice of the word colligative to describe these properties.

4. Distinguish between volatile and nonvolatile substances.

5. What effect does the presence of a nonvolatile solute have upon the freezing point of a solution?

6. Explain the difference between molarity and molality. What are the units on each?

7. What is the freezing point (°C) of a solution prepared by dissolving 15.6 g of $Al(NO_3)_3$ in 150 g of water? The molal freezing point depression constant for water is 1.86 °C/m. Assume complete dissociation of the $Al(NO_3)_3$.

8. What is the molality of a solution that contains 5.2 g of urea (molar mass = 60 g/mol) in 250 g of benzene (C_6H_6)?

9. Calculate the freezing point of a solution containing 1.25 g of benzene (C_6H_6) in 100 g of chloroform $(CHCl_3)$.

10. A solution containing 0.050 g of an unknown nonelectrolyte in 2.50 g of cyclohexane was found to freeze at 5.1 °C. What is the molar mass of the unknown substance?

11. How many grams of $NaNO_3$ would you add to 500 g of H_2O to prepare a solution that is 0.500 m in $NaNO_3$?

Name _____ Desk _____

Date _____ Laboratory Instructor _____

REPORT SHEET | EXPERIMENT

Freezing Point Depression | 2

A. Preparation of Experimental Apparatus and Freezing Point Determination of Lauric Acid

1. Mass of freezing point depression apparatus   _____
2. Mass of freezing point depression apparatus with lauric acid   _____
3. Mass of lauric acid used   _____

B. Freezing Point Determination of a Lauric Acid Solution

4. Designation of unknown   _____
5. Mass of added unknown, Exp. 3   _____
6. Mass of added unknown, Exp. 4   _____

Freezing point of lauric acid from Part A, Exp. 1   _____

Freezing point of lauric acid from Part A, Exp. 2   _____

Average freezing point of lauric acid   _____

Freezing point of lauric acid and unknown from Part B, Exp. 3   _____

Freezing point of lauric acid and unknown from Part B, Exp. 4   _____

$\Delta T_f = T_{f,mixture} - T_{f,pure}$ Exp. 3 _____   Exp. 4 _____

Solution molality (show calculations)   Exp. 3 _____   Exp. 4 _____

Moles of unknown (show calculation)   Exp. 3 _____   Exp. 4 _____

Molar mass of unknown (show calculation)   Exp. 3 _____   Exp. 4 _____

Average molar mass   _____

Show your calculations for the solution molality, mole of unknown, and molar mass of unknown.

Hand in your cooling curves with your report sheet.

Pure lauric acid

	Exp. 1		**Exp. 2**
Time (seconds)	**Temperature (°C)**	**Time (seconds)**	**Temperature (°C)**
0	_____	0	_____
30	_____	30	_____
60	_____	60	_____
90	_____	90	_____
120	_____	120	_____
150	_____	150	_____
180	_____	180	_____
210	_____	210	_____
240	_____	240	_____
270	_____	270	_____
300	_____	300	_____
330	_____	330	_____
360	_____	360	_____
390	_____	390	_____
420	_____	420	_____
450	_____	450	_____
480	_____	480	_____
510	_____	510	_____
540	_____	540	_____
570	_____	570	_____
600	_____	600	_____
630	_____	630	_____
660	_____	660	_____
690	_____	690	_____
720	_____	720	_____
750	_____	750	_____
780	_____	780	_____

Solution of lauric acid and unknown (data are for camphor)

Exp. 3		Exp. 4	
Time (seconds)	**Temperature (°C)**	**Time (seconds)**	**Temperature (°C)**
0	_____	0	_____
30	_____	30	_____
60	_____	60	_____
90	_____	90	_____
120	_____	120	_____
150	_____	150	_____
180	_____	180	_____
210	_____	210	_____
240	_____	240	_____
270	_____	270	_____
300	_____	300	_____
330	_____	330	_____
360	_____	360	_____
390	_____	390	_____
420	_____	420	_____
450	_____	450	_____
480	_____	480	_____
510	_____	510	_____
540	_____	540	_____
570	_____	570	_____
600	_____	600	_____
630	_____	630	_____
660	_____	660	_____
690	_____	690	_____
720	_____	720	_____
750	_____	750	_____
780	_____	780	_____

QUESTIONS

1. What are the major sources of error in this experiment?

2. Suppose throughout the experiment, your thermometer consistently read a temperature 1.2 °C lower than the correct temperature. How would this have affected the molar mass you found?

3. At equal concentrations, would a nonelectrolyte (e.g. glucose) or electrolyte (e.g. NaCl) containing solution have a lower freezing point? Why?

4. Arrange the following liquids in order of increasing freezing point (lowest to highest temperature): pure H_2O, aqueous NaF (0.31 m), aqueous glucose (0.60 m), aqueous sucrose (0.50 m), aqueous MgI_2 (0.22 m)

5. If the freezing point of the solution had been incorrectly read 0.3 °C lower than the true freezing point, would the calculated molar mass of the solute have been too high or too low? Explain your answer.

6. What mass of NaCl is dissolved in 200 g of water in a 0.100 m solution?

7. Calculate the molalities of some commercial reagents from the following data:

	HCl(aq)	**NH$_3$(aq)**
Formula weight (g/mol)	36.465	17.03
Density of solution (g/mL)	1.19	0.90
Weight %	37.2	28.0
Molarity	12.1	14.8

8. A solution containing 1.00 g of an unknown nonelectrolyte liquid and 9.00 g water has a freezing point of −3.33 °C. The K_f = 1.86 °C/m for water. Calculate the molar mass of the unknown liquid in g/mol.

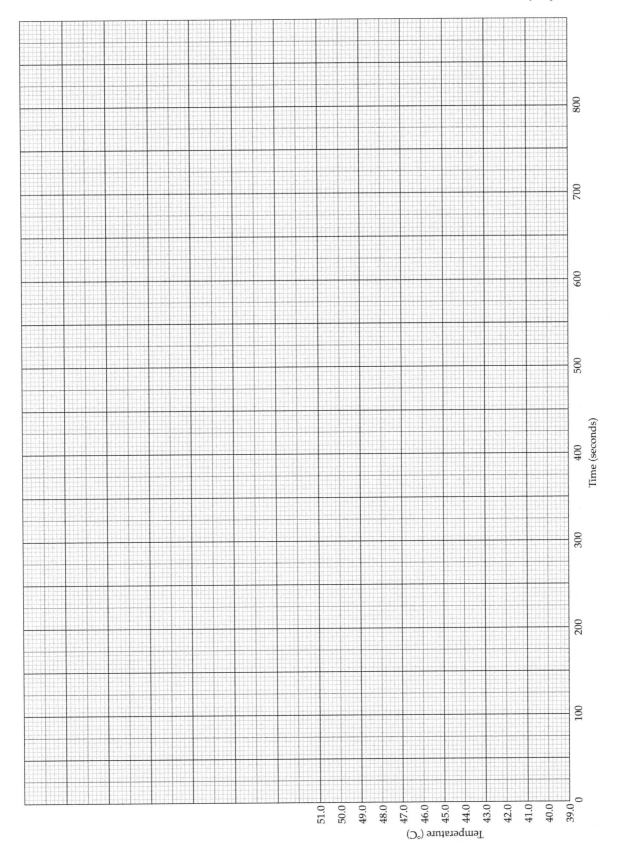

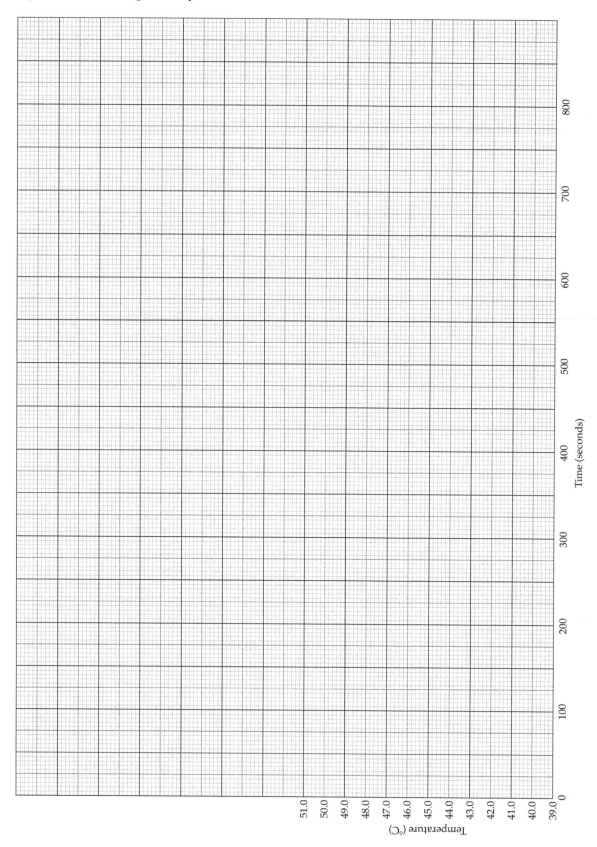

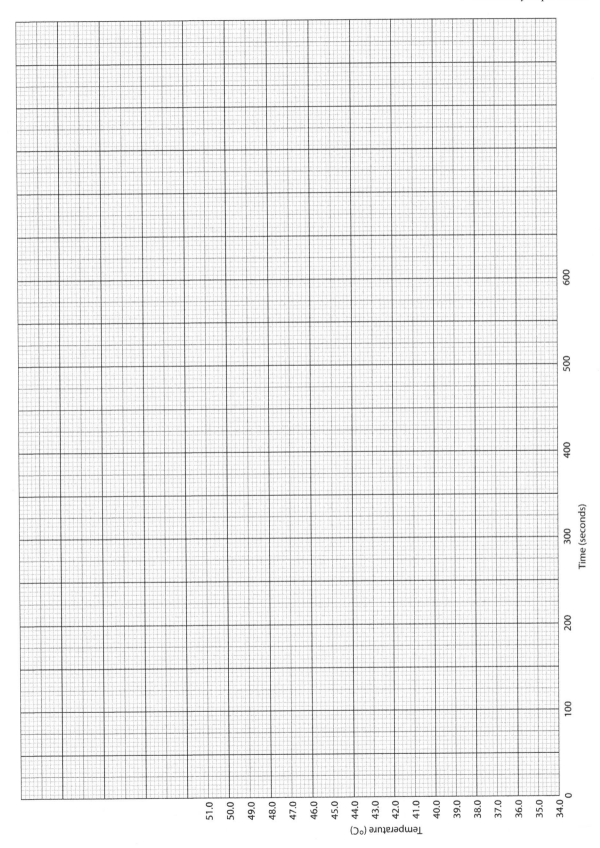

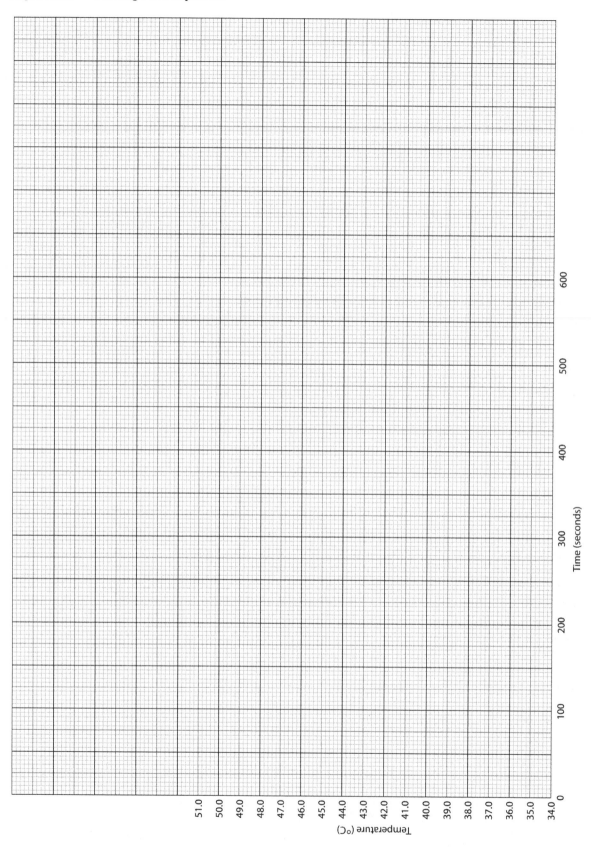

Time (seconds)

Temperature (°C)

Rates of Chemical Reactions I: A Clock Reaction

To measure the effect of concentration upon the rate of the reaction of peroxydisulfate ion with iodide ion; to determine the order of the reaction with respect to the reactant concentrations; and to obtain the rate law for the chemical reaction.

OBJECTIVE

Apparatus

burets (2)
1 mL volumetric pipets (2)
clock or watch with second hand
pipet bulb
buret clamp
ring stand

25 mL volumetric pipet
50 mL volumetric pipet
test tubes (8)
250 mL Erlenmeyer flasks (4)
100 mL beakers (4)

APPARATUS AND CHEMICALS

Chemicals

0.200 M KI

1% starch solution, boiled

0.200 M $(NH_4)_2S_2O_8$
  (freshly prepared)

0.400 M $Na_2S_2O_3$ (freshly prepared)

0.1 M solution of Na_2H_2EDTA

0.200 M KNO_3

WORK IN PAIRS, BUT EVALUATE YOUR DATA INDIVIDUALLY.

Factors Affecting Rates of Reactions

DISCUSSION

On the basis of the experiments you've performed, you may have noticed that reactions occur at varying rates. There is an entire spectrum of rates of reactions, ranging from very slow to extremely fast. For example, the rusting of iron is reasonably slow, whereas the decomposition of TNT is extremely fast. The branch of chemistry concerned with the rates of reactions is called *chemical kinetics*. Experiments show that rates of homogeneous reactions in solution depend upon the following:

1. The nature of the reactants
2. The concentration of the reactants
3. The temperature
4. The presence of a catalyst

   Before a reaction can occur, the reactants must come in direct contact via collisions of the reacting particles. However, even then, the reacting particles (ions or molecules) must collide with sufficient energy to result in a reaction. If they do not, their collisions are ineffective and analogous to collisions of billiard balls. Keeping these considerations in mind, you can qualitatively explain how the various factors influence the rates of reactions.

Concentration Changing the concentration of a solution alters the number of particles per unit volume. The more particles present in a given volume, the greater the probability of their colliding. Hence, increasing the concentration of a solution increases the number of collisions per unit time and therefore may increase the rate of reaction.

Temperature Because temperature is a measure of the average kinetic energy, an increase in temperature increases the kinetic energy of the particles. An increase in kinetic energy increases the velocity of the particles and therefore the number of collisions between them in a *given period of time*. Thus, the rate of reaction increases. Also, an increase in kinetic energy results in a greater proportion of the collisions having the required activation energy for the reaction. As a rule of thumb, for each 10 °C increase in temperature, the rate of reaction doubles.

Catalyst Catalysts, in some cases, are believed to increase reaction rates by bringing particles into close juxtaposition in the correct geometrical arrangement for reaction to occur. In other instances, catalysts offer an alternative route to the reaction, one that requires less energetic collisions between reactant particles. If less energy is required for a successful collision, a larger percentage of the collisions will have the requisite energy, and the reaction will occur faster. Actually, the catalyst may take an active part in the reaction, but at the end of the reaction, the catalyst can be recovered chemically unchanged.

Order of Reaction Defined

Now examine precisely what is meant by the expression *rate of reaction*. Consider the hypothetical reaction

$$A + B \longrightarrow C + D \qquad\qquad [1]$$

You can measure the rate of this reaction by observing the rate of disappearance of either of the reactants A and B or the rate of appearance of either of the products C and D. In practice, then, you measure the change of concentration with time of A, B, C, or D. Which species you choose to observe is a matter of convenience. For example, if A, B, and D are colorless and C is colored, you could conveniently measure the rate of appearance of C by observing an increase in the intensity of the color of the solution as a function of time. Mathematically, the rate of reaction may be expressed as follows:

$$\text{rate of disappearance of A} = \frac{\text{change in concentration of A}}{\text{time required for change}} = \frac{-\Delta[A]}{\Delta t}$$

$$\text{rate of appearance of C} = \frac{\text{change in concentration of C}}{\text{time required for change}} = \frac{\Delta[C]}{\Delta t}$$

In general, the rate of the reaction will depend upon the concentrations of the reactants. Thus, the rate of the hypothetical reaction may be expressed as

$$\text{rate} = k[A]^x[B]^y \qquad\qquad [2]$$

where [A] and [B] are the molar concentrations of A and B, x and y are the powers to which the respective concentrations must be raised to describe the rate, and k is the *specific rate constant*. One of the objectives of chemical kinetics is to determine the rate law. Stated slightly differently, one goal of measuring the rate of the reaction is to determine the numerical values of x and y in Equation [2]. Suppose you found that $x = 2$ and $y = 1$ for this reaction. Then

$$\text{rate} = k[A]^2[B] \qquad [3]$$

would be the rate law. It should be evident from Equation [3] that doubling the concentration of B (keeping [A] the same) would cause the reaction rate to double. On the other hand, doubling the concentration of A (keeping [B] the same) would cause the rate to increase by a factor of 4 because the rate of the reaction is proportional to the *square* of the concentration of A. The powers to which the concentrations in the rate law are raised are termed the *order of the reaction*. In this case, the reaction is said to be second order in A and first order in B. The *overall order* of the reaction is the sum of the exponents, $2 + 1 = 3$, or a third-order reaction. It is possible to determine the order of the reaction by noting the effects of changing reagent concentrations on the rate of the reaction. Note that the order of a reaction may be (and frequently is) different from the stoichiometry of the reaction.

Keep in mind that k, the specific rate constant, has a definite value that is independent of the concentration. It is characteristic of a given reaction and depends upon temperature only. Once that rate law and the rate are known, the value of k can be calculated.

Reaction of Peroxydisulfate Ion with Iodide Ion

In this experiment, you will measure the rate of the reaction

$$S_2O_8^{2-}(aq) + 2I^-(aq) \longrightarrow I_2(aq) + 2SO_4^{2-}(aq) \qquad [4]$$

and you will determine the rate law by measuring the amount of peroxydisulfate, $S_2O_8^{2-}$, that reacts as a function of time. The rate law to be determined is of the form

$$\text{rate of disappearance of } S_2O_8^{2-} = k[S_2O_8^{2-}]^x[I^-]^y \qquad [5]$$

or

$$\frac{\Delta[S_2O_8^{2-}]}{\Delta t} = k[S_2O_8^{2-}]^x[I^-]^y$$

Your goal will be to determine the values of x and y as well as the specific rate constant, k.

You will add to the solution a small amount of another reagent (sodium thiosulfate, $Na_2S_2O_3$), which will cause a change in the color of the solution. The amount is such that the color change will occur when 2×10^{-4} mol of $S_2O_8^{2-}$ has reacted. For reasons to be explained shortly, the solution will turn blue-black when 2×10^{-4} mol of $S_2O_8^{2-}$ has reacted. You will quickly add another portion of $Na_2S_2O_3$ after the appearance of the color, and the blue-black color will disappear. When the blue-black color reappears the second time, *another* 2×10^{-4} mol of $S_2O_8^{2-}$ has reacted, making a total of $2(2 \times 10^{-4})$ mol of $S_2O_8^{2-}$ that has reacted. You will repeat this procedure several times, keeping *careful* note of the time for the appearance of the blue-black colors.

By graphing the amount of $S_2O_8^{2-}$ consumed versus time, you will be able to determine the rate of the reaction. By changing the initial concentrations of $S_2O_8^{2-}$ and I^- and observing the effects upon the rate of the reaction, you will determine the order of the reaction with respect to $S_2O_8^{2-}$ and I^-.

The blue-black color that appears in the reaction is due to the presence of a starch–iodine complex that is formed from iodine, I_2, and starch in the solution. Therefore, the color will not appear until a detectable amount of I_2 is formed according to Equation [4]. The thiosulfate that is added to the solution reacts *extremely rapidly* with the iodine, as follows:

$$I_2(aq) + 2S_2O_3^{2-}(aq) \longrightarrow 2I^-(aq) + S_4O_6^{2-}(aq) \tag{6}$$

Consequently, until all of the $S_2O_3^{2-}$ that is added is consumed, there will not be a sufficient amount of I_2 in the solution to yield the blue-black color. You will add 4×10^{-4} mol of $S_2O_3^{2-}$ each time (these equal portions are termed *aliquots*). From the stoichiometry of Equations [4] and [6], you can verify that when this quantity of $S_2O_3^{2-}$ has reacted, 2×10^{-4} mol of $S_2O_8^{2-}$ has reacted. Note also that although iodide, I^-, is consumed according to Equation [4], it is rapidly regenerated according to Equation [6]; therefore, its concentration does not change during a given experiment.

Graphical Determination of Rate

The more rapidly the 2×10^{-4} mol of $S_2O_8^{2-}$ is consumed, the faster the reaction. To determine the rate of the reaction, a plot of moles of $S_2O_8^{2-}$ that have reacted versus the time required for the reaction is made, as shown in Figure 3.1. The best straight line passing through the origin is drawn, and the slope is determined. The slope, $\Delta S_2O_8^{2-}/\Delta t$, corresponds to the moles of $S_2O_8^{2-}$ that have been consumed per second and is proportional to the rate. Because the rate corresponds to the change in the concentration of $S_2O_8^{2-}$ per second, dividing the slope by the volume of the solution yields the rate of disappearance of $S_2O_8^{2-}$ (that is, $\Delta[S_2O_8^{2-}]/\Delta t$). If the total volume of the solution in this example was 75 mL, the rate would be as follows:

$$\frac{4.5 \times 10^{-5} \text{ mol/s}}{0.075 \text{ L}} = 6.0 \times 10^{-4} \text{ mol/L-s}$$

If you obtain a rate of 6.0×10^{-4} mol/L-s when $[S_2O_8^{2-}] = 2.0\,M$ and $[I^-] = 2.0\,M$ and a rate of 3.0×10^{-4} mol/L-s when $[S_2O_8^{2-}] = 1.0\,M$ and $[I^-] = 2.0\,M$, you know that doubling the concentration of $S_2O_8^{2-}$ doubles the rate of the reaction and the reaction is first order in $S_2O_8^{2-}$. By varying the initial concentrations of $S_2O_8^{2-}$ and I^-, you can, via the above type of analysis, determine the order of the reaction with respect to both species.

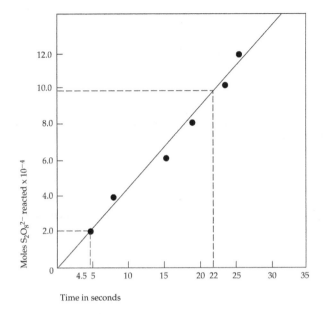

$$\text{Slope} = \frac{\Delta S_2O_8{}^{2-}}{\Delta t}$$

$$= \frac{(9.8 - 2.0) \times 10^{-4}\,\text{mol}}{(22.0 - 4.5)\,\text{s}}$$

$$= \frac{7.8 \times 10^{-4}\,\text{mol}}{17.5\,\text{s}}$$

$$= 4.5 \times 10^{-5}\,\text{mol/s}$$

or use a linear regression analysis to determine the slope (see Appendix C)

▲**FIGURE 3.1** Graphical determination of rate.

GIVE IT SOME THOUGHT

What does the steepness of the slope tell you about the rate of the reaction?

Helpful Comments

1. According to the procedure of this experiment, the solution will turn blue-black when exactly 2×10^{-4} mol of $S_2O_8{}^{2-}$ has reacted.

2. The purpose of the KNO_3 solution in this reaction is to keep the *reaction medium* the same in each run in terms of the concentration of ions; it does not enter into the reaction in any way.

3. The reaction studied in this experiment is catalyzed by metal ions. The purpose of the drop of the EDTA solution is to minimize the effects of trace quantities of metal ion impurities that would cause spurious effects on the reaction.

4. You will perform a few preliminary experiments to become acquainted with the observations in this experiment so that you will know what to expect in the reactions.

5. The initial concentrations of the reactants have been provided on the report sheet.

A. Preliminary Experiments

PROCEDURE

1. Dilute 5.0 mL of 0.2 *M* KI solution with 10.0 mL of distilled water in a test tube, add three drops of starch solution and mix thoroughly, and then add 5.0 mL of 0.2 *M* $(NH_4)_2S_2O_8$ solution. Mix. Wait awhile and observe color changes.

2. Repeat the procedure in (1), but when the solution changes color, add four drops of 0.4 M $Na_2S_2O_3$, mix the solution, and note the effect that the addition of $Na_2S_2O_3$ has on the color.

B. Kinetics Experiment

Equipment Setup Set up two burets held by a clamp on a ring stand as shown in Figure 3.2. Use these burets to accurately measure the volumes of the KI and KNO_3 solutions. Use two separate 1 mL pipets for measuring the volumes of the $Na_2S_2O_3$ and starch solutions and use 25 mL and 50 mL pipets to measure the volumes of the $(NH_4)_2S_2O_8$ solutions.

Solution Preparation Prepare four reaction solutions as follows (prepare the next solution only when you have completely finished with the previous one):

Each solution must be freshly prepared before you to begin the rate study—that is, *prepare solutions 1, 2, 3, and 4 one at a time as you make your measurements.*

Solution 1: 25.0 mL KI solution
           1.0 mL starch solution
           1.0 mL $Na_2S_2O_3$ solution
           48.0 mL KNO_3 solution
           1 drop EDTA solution
Total volume = 75.0 mL

Solution 3: 50.0 mL KI solution
           1.0 mL starch solution
           1.0 mL $Na_2S_2O_3$ solution
           23.0 mL KNO_3 solution
           1 drop EDTA solution
Total volume = 75.0 mL

Solution 2: 25.0 mL KI solution
           1.0 mL starch solution
           1.0 mL $Na_2S_2O_3$ solution
           23.0 mL KNO_3 solution
           1 drop EDTA solution
Total volume = 50.0 mL

Solution 4: 12.5 mL KI solution
           1.0 mL starch solution
           1.0 mL $Na_2S_2O_3$ solution
           35.5 mL KNO_3 solution
           1 drop EDTA solution
Total volume = 50.0 mL

  GIVE IT SOME THOUGHT
Why is a drop of EDTA added to each solution?

Rate Measurements Prepare solution 1 in a 250 mL Erlenmeyer flask that has been scrupulously cleaned and dried. Pipet 25.0 mL of $(NH_4)_2S_2O_8$ solution into a clean, dry 100 mL beaker. *Be ready* to begin timing the reaction when the solutions are mixed (READ AHEAD). The reaction starts the moment the solutions are mixed. BE PREPARED! ZERO TIME! Quickly pour the 25.0 mL of $(NH_4)_2S_2O_8$ solution into solution 1 and swirl vigorously; note to the nearest second the time you begin mixing. At the instant the blue-black color appears, 2×10^{-4} mol of $S_2O_8^{2-}$ has reacted. *Immediately* (be prepared!) add a 1 mL aliquot of $Na_2S_2O_3$ solution from the pipet and swirl the solution; the color will disappear. By filling each of seven clean, dry test tubes with 1 mL of $Na_2S_2O_3$ solution, to avoid losing time, you can add these aliquots to your reactions when the blue color appears.

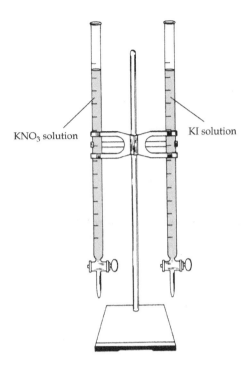

KNO₃ solution

KI solution

▲ **FIGURE 3.2** Experimental apparatus with two burets clamped to a ring stand.

Record the time for the reappearance of the blue-black color. Add another 1 mL aliquot of $Na_2S_2O_3$ solution and note the time for the reappearance of the color. The time interval being measured is that between appearances of the blue-black color. For good results, these aliquots of $Na_2S_2O_3$ must be measured as quickly, accurately, and reproducibly as possible. Continue this procedure until you have added seven aliquots to solution 1.

 GIVE IT SOME THOUGHT

What does the blue-black color indicate?

You are finished with solution 1 when you have recorded all of your times on the report sheet. *(The time intervals are cumulative.)*

Solutions 2, 3, and 4 should be treated in the same manner except that 50.0 mL portions of $(NH_4)_2S_2O_8$ solutions should be added to solutions 2 and 4 and 25 mL of $(NH_4)_2S_2O_8$ solution should be added to solution 3. **(CAUTION: *Be on guard—solution 2 will react more rapidly than solution 1.*)** In each of these reactions, the final total solution volume is exactly 100 mL.

Calculations

Use the data sheet to tabulate the following for each aliquot of $Na_2S_2O_3$ added to each of the four solutions:

1. The time interval from the start of the reaction (addition of $S_2O_8^{2-}$) to the appearance of color for the first aliquot of $S_2O_3^{2-}$ and the time interval from the preceding color appearance for each succeeding aliquot (column 2).

2. The cumulative time from the start of the reaction to each appearance of color (column 3).

3. The corresponding numbers of moles $S_2O_8^{2-}$ consumed (column 4).

For each solution, use the graph paper provided to plot the moles of $S_2O_8^{2-}$ consumed (as the ordinate, vertical axis) versus time in seconds (as the abscissa, horizontal axis), using the data in columns 3 and 4 on the report sheet. Calculate the slope of each plot and from these calculations, answer the questions on your report sheet.

 GIVE IT SOME THOUGHT

    a. Do you expect your graph to be linear or exponential?
    b. What does this tell you about the overall order?

Waste-Disposal Instructions No wastes from this experiment should be flushed down the sink. Locate the special containers placed in the laboratory for the disposal of excess iodide and peroxydisulfate solutions as well as for the reaction mixtures from the test tubes or flasks. All wastes should be disposed of in these containers.

Rates of Chemical Reactions I: A Clock Reaction | 3 | Pre-lab Questions

Before beginning this experiment in the laboratory, you should be able to answer the following questions.

1. What factors influence the rate of a chemical reaction?

2. What is the general form of a rate law?

3. What is the order of reaction with respect to A and B for a reaction that obeys the rate law: rate $= k[A]^2[B]^3$?

4. Write the chemical equations involved in this experiment and show that the rate of disappearance of $[S_2O_8^{2-}]$ is proportional to the rate of appearance of the blue-black color of the starch–iodine complex.

5. It is found for the reaction $A + B \longrightarrow C$ that doubling the concentration of either A or B quadruples the rate of the reaction. Write the rate law for this reaction.

6. If 2.0×10^{-4} moles of $S_2O_8^{2-}$ in 50 mL of solution is consumed in 188 seconds, what is the rate of consumption of $S_2O_8^{2-}$?

7. Why are chemists concerned with the rates of chemical reactions? What possible practical value does this type of information have?

8. Suppose you were dissolving a metal such as zinc with hydrochloric acid. How would the particle size of the zinc affect the rate of its dissolution?

9. Assuming that a chemical reaction doubles in rate for each 10 °C temperature increase, by what factor would the rate increase if the temperature increased 40 °C?

10. A reaction between substances A and B has been found to give the following data:

$$3A + 2B \longrightarrow 2C + D$$

[A] (mol/L)	[B] (mol/L)	Rate of appearance of C (mol/L-hr)
1.0×10^{-2}	1.0	0.300×10^{-6}
1.0×10^{-2}	3.0	8.10×10^{-6}
2.0×10^{-2}	3.0	3.24×10^{-5}
2.0×10^{-2}	1.0	1.20×10^{-6}
3.0×10^{-2}	3.0	7.30×10^{-5}

Using the above data, determine the order of the reaction with respect to A and B, the rate law, and calculate the specific rate constant.

Name _____ Desk _____

Date _____ Laboratory Instructor _____

REPORT SHEET | EXPERIMENT

Rates of Chemical Reactions I: A Clock Reaction

3

A. Preliminary Experiments

1. What are the colors of the solutions containing the following ions? K^+ _____ ; I^- _____

2. The color of the starch $\cdot I_2$ complex is _____ .

B. Kinetics Experiment

Solution 1. Initial $[S_2O_8^{2-}] = 0.050\ M$; initial $[I^-] = 0.050\ M$. Time experiment started _____

Aliquot no.	Time (s) between appearances of color	Cumulative times (s)	Total moles of $S_2O_8^{2-}$ consumed
1	_____	_____	2.0×10^{-4}
2	_____	_____	4.0×10^{-4}
3	_____	_____	6.0×10^{-4}
4	_____	_____	8.0×10^{-4}
5	_____	_____	$10. \times 10^{-4}$
6	_____	_____	12×10^{-4}
7	_____	_____	14×10^{-4}

Solution 2. Initial $[S_2O_8^{2-}] = 0.10\ M$; initial $[I^-] = 0.050\ M$. Time experiment started _____

Aliquot no.	Time (s) between appearances of color	Cumulative times (s)	Total moles of $S_2O_8^{2-}$ consumed
1	_____	_____	2.0×10^{-4}
2	_____	_____	4.0×10^{-4}
3	_____	_____	6.0×10^{-4}
4	_____	_____	8.0×10^{-4}
5	_____	_____	$10. \times 10^{-4}$
6	_____	_____	12×10^{-4}
7	_____	_____	14×10^{-4}

Solution 3. Initial $[S_2O_8^{2-}] = 0.050\ M$; initial $[I^-] = 0.10\ M$. Time experiment started _____

Aliquot no.	Time (s) between appearances of color	Cumulative times (s)	Total moles of $S_2O_8^{2-}$ consumed
1	_____	_____	2.0×10^{-4}
2	_____	_____	4.0×10^{-4}
3	_____	_____	6.0×10^{-4}
4	_____	_____	8.0×10^{-4}
5	_____	_____	$10. \times 10^{-4}$
6	_____	_____	12×10^{-4}
7	_____	_____	14×10^{-4}

Solution 4. Initial $[S_2O_8^{2-}] = 0.10\ M$; initial $[I^-] = 0.025\ M$. Time experiment started _____

Aliquot no.	Time (s) between appearances of color	Cumulative times (s)	Total moles of $S_2O_8^{2-}$ consumed
1	_____	_____	2.0×10^{-4}
2	_____	_____	4.0×10^{-4}
3	_____	_____	6.0×10^{-4}
4	_____	_____	8.0×10^{-4}
5	_____	_____	$10. \times 10^{-4}$
6	_____	_____	12×10^{-4}
7	_____	_____	14×10^{-4}

Calculations

1. Rate of reaction, $\Delta[S_2O_8^{2-}]/\Delta t$, as calculated from graphs (that is, from slopes of lines):

   Solution 1 _____   Solution 3 _____

   Solution 2 _____   Solution 4 _____

2. What effect does doubling the concentration of I^- have on the rate of this reaction?

3. What effect does changing the $[S_2O_8^{2-}]$ have on the reaction?

4. Write the rate law for this reaction that is consistent with your data.

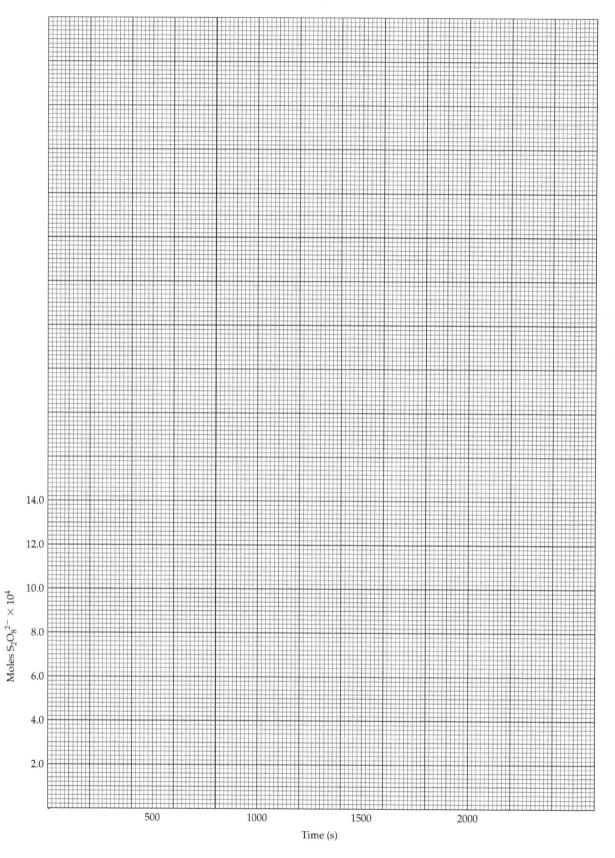

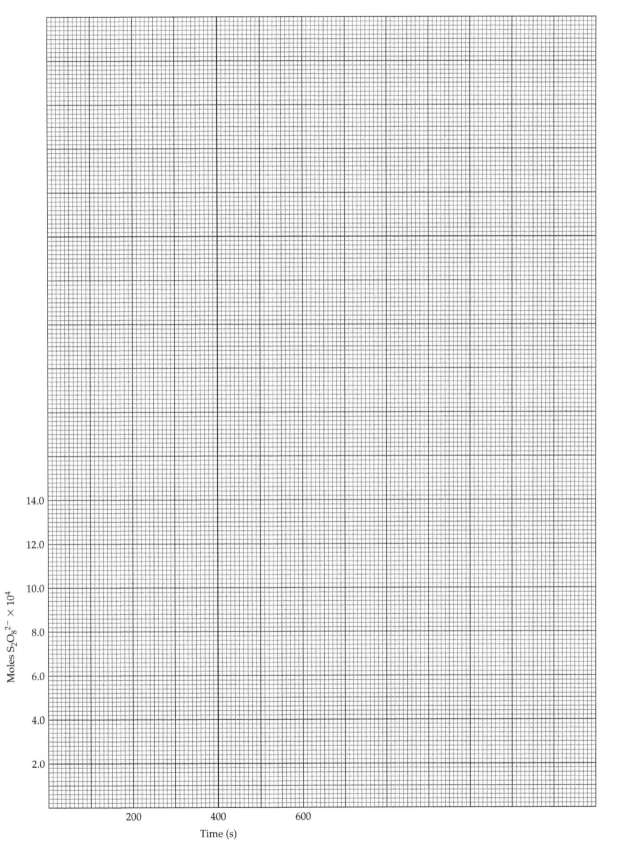

Moles $S_2O_8^{2-} \times 10^4$

Time (s)

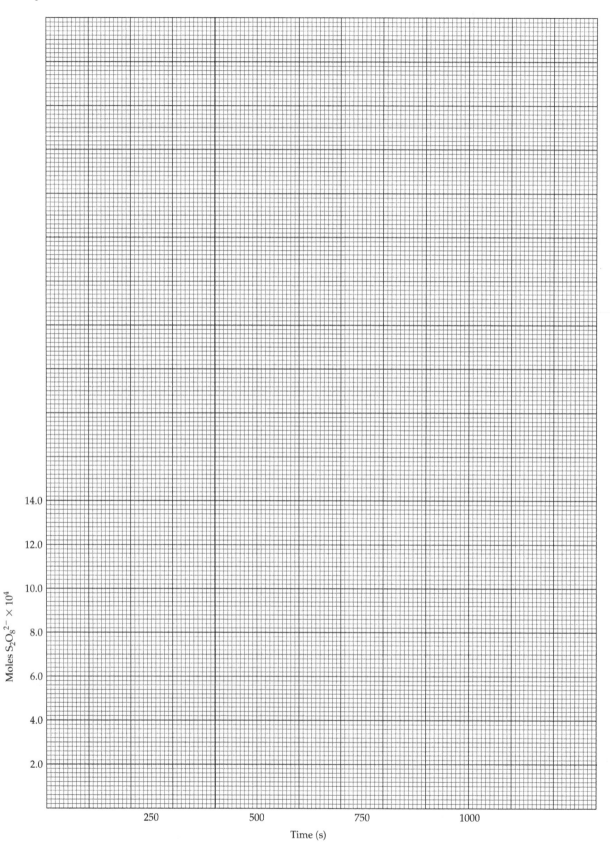

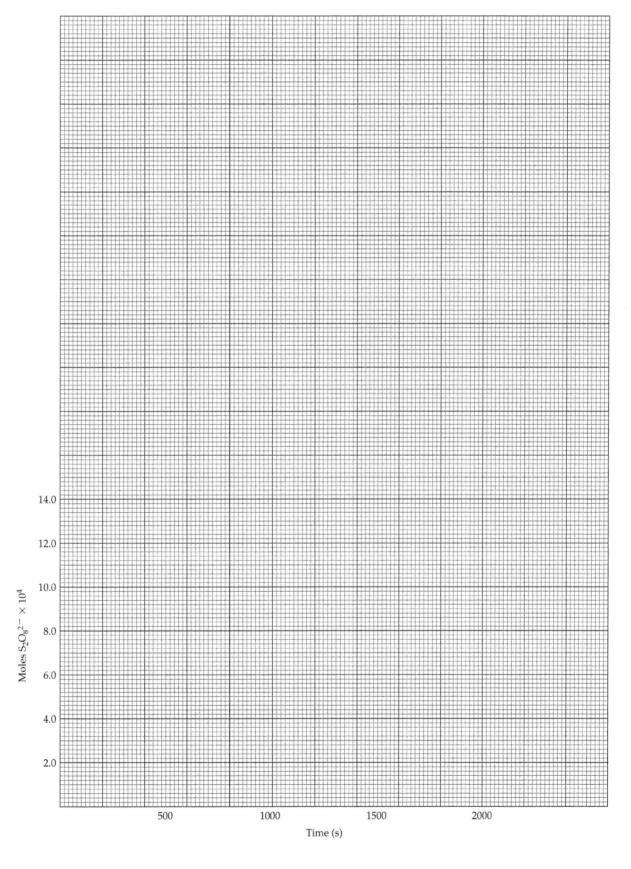

Chemical Equilibrium: Le Châtelier's Principle

4

To study the effects of concentration and temperature on equilibrium positions.

OBJECTIVE

Apparatus

medicine droppers (4)	large test tube (1)
250 mL beaker	ring stand, iron ring, and wire gauze
100 mL graduated cylinder	
small test tubes (3)	Bunsen burner and hose

APPARATUS AND CHEMICALS

Chemicals

0.1 M CuSO$_4$	0.01 M AgNO$_3$
0.1 M NiCl$_2$	6 M HNO$_3$
1.0 M CoCl$_2$	0.1 M HCl
0.1 M KI	1 M HCl
0.1 M Na$_2$CO$_3$	15 M NH$_3$

DISCUSSION

Many chemical reactions do not go to completion, that is, do not produce 100% yield of products. After a certain amount of time, many of these reactions appear to "stop"—colors stop changing, gases stop evolving, etc. In several of these instances, the process apparently stops before the reaction is complete, leading to a mixture of reactants and products.

For example, consider the interconversion of gaseous nitrogen oxides in a sealed tube.

$$N_2O_4(g) \rightleftharpoons 2NO_2(g) \qquad [1]$$
$$\text{colorless} \qquad \text{brown}$$

When frozen N$_2$O$_4$ is warmed above its boiling point (21.2 °C), the gas in a sealed tube progressively turns darker as colorless N$_2$O$_4$ dissociates into brown NO$_2$. The color change eventually stops even though N$_2$O$_4$ is still present in the tube.

The condition in which the concentrations of all reactants and products in a closed system cease to change with time is called *chemical equilibrium*. Chemical equilibrium occurs when the rate at which products are formed from reactants equals the rate at which reactants are formed from products. For equilibrium to occur, neither reactants nor products can escape from the system.

If the concentration of any one of the reactants or products involved in a chemical equilibrium is changed or if the temperature is changed, the position of the equilibrium shifts to *minimize the change*. For example, assuming that the reaction represented by Equation [1] is at equilibrium, if more NO$_2$ is added, the probability of it reacting with other NO$_2$ molecules is increased, and the concentration of NO_2 decreases until a new state of equilibrium is attained. The equilibrium reaction is said to *shift to the left*. *Le Châtelier's principle* states that if a system at equilibrium is disturbed (by altering the concentration of reactants or products, the temperature, or the pressure), the equilibrium will shift to minimize the disturbing influence. By this principle, if a reactant or product is added to a system at equilibrium, the equilibrium will shift to consume the added substance. Conversely, if reactant or product is removed, the equilibrium will shift to replenish the substance that was removed. The enthalpy change for a reaction indicates how a change in temperature affects the equilibrium. For an endothermic reaction in the forward direction, an increase in temperature shifts the equilibrium to the right to absorb the added heat; for an exothermic reaction in the forward direction, an increase in temperature shifts the equilibrium to the left. The equilibrium of Equation [1] is endothermic, $\Delta H = +58$ kJ. Increasing the temperature will shift this equilibrium in the direction that absorbs the heat; so the equilibrium shifts to the right.

GIVE IT SOME THOUGHT

If this reaction happened to have a negative ΔH, which way would the equilibrium shift?

It is important to remember that changes in concentrations, while causing shifts in the equilibrium positions, do not cause a change in the value of the equilibrium constant. Only changes in temperature affect the values of equilibrium constants.

In this experiment, you will observe two ways that a chemical equilibrium can be disturbed: (1) by adding or removing a reactant or product and (2) by changing the temperature. You will interpret your observations and conclusions using Le Châtelier's principle.

Part I: Changes in Reactant or Product Concentrations
A. Copper and Nickel Ions

Aqueous solutions of copper(II) and nickel(II) appear blue and green, respectively. However, when aqueous ammonia, NH_3, is added to these solutions, their colors change to dark blue and pale violet, respectively.

$$[Cu(H_2O)_4]^{2+}(aq) + 4NH_3(aq) \rightleftharpoons [Cu(NH_3)_4]^{2+}(aq) + 4H_2O(l)$$
blue   dark blue

$$[Ni(H_2O)_6]^{2+}(aq) + 6NH_3(aq) \rightleftharpoons [Ni(NH_3)_6]^{2+}(aq) + 6H_2O(l)$$
green   pale violet

Ammonia substitutes for water in these two reactions because the metal–ammonia bond is stronger than the metal–water bond, and the equilibria shift to the right, accounting for the color changes.

If a strong acid such as HCl is added to these ammoniacal solutions, their colors revert back to the original colors of blue and green. The equilibria shift left because the reactant ammonia, NH_3, is removed from the equilibria. It reacts with the acid to form ammonium ion according to reaction [2].

$$H^+(aq) + NH_3(aq) \rightleftharpoons NH_4^+(aq) \qquad [2]$$

Place about 1 mL of 0.1 M $CuSO_4$ in a small, clean test tube. Record the color of the solution on your report sheet (1). (**CAUTION**: *Concentrated* NH_3 *has a strong irritating odor; do not inhale. If you come in contact with it, immediately wash the area with copious amounts of water.*) Add 15 M NH_3 dropwise until a color change occurs and the solution is clear, not colorless. Some solid may initially form because $Cu(OH)_2$ is sparingly soluble. It will dissolve as more $NH_3(aq)$ is added. Record your observation on your report sheet (2). Mix the solution in the test tube by "tickling" the test tube with your fingers as you add the NH_3. Add 1 M HCl dropwise while carefully mixing the solution in the test tube until the solution becomes clear and the color changes. Note the color (3).

GIVE IT SOME THOUGHT

a. When concentrated NH_3 is added to $[Ni(H_2O)_6]^{2+}$, which way will the equilibrium shift?

b. Which way will it shift when HCl is added?

Repeat the same procedure using 0.1 M $NiCl_2$ in place of the $CuSO_4$ and record your corresponding observations on your report sheet (4–6).

Dispose of the solutions in the test tubes in the designated waste containers.

B. Cobalt Ions

Cobalt(II) ions in aqueous solution appear pale pink. In the presence of a large concentration of chloride ions, the solution changes color to blue and the following equilibrium is established:

$$[Co(H_2O)_6]^{2+}(aq) + 4Cl^-(aq) \rightleftharpoons [CoCl_4]^{2-}(aq) + 6H_2O(l) \qquad [3]$$

pale pink   deep blue

GIVE IT SOME THOUGHT

a. When you add 12 M HCl, which concentrations are affected in Equation [3]?

b. How will this shift the equilibrium?

Place about 0.5 mL (10 drops) of 1 M $CoCl_2$ in a small, clean test tube and note the color (8). (**CAUTION**: *Avoid inhalation and contact with concentrated HCl. If you come in contact with it, immediately wash the area with copious amounts of water.*) Add dropwise 12 M HCl to the test tube until a distinct color change occurs. Record the color on your report sheet (9). Slowly add water to the test tube while mixing. Record the color change on your report sheet (10).

Dispose of the solution in the test tube in the designated waste container.

Part II. Equilibria Involving Sparingly Soluble Salts

Silver carbonate, silver chloride, and silver iodide salts are only very slightly soluble in water. They can be precipitated from silver nitrate solutions by the addition of sodium salts containing the corresponding anions. For example, silver carbonate will precipitate by the mixing of solutions of $AgNO_3$ and Na_2CO_3:

$$2AgNO_3(aq) + Na_2CO_3(aq) \rightleftharpoons Ag_2CO_3(s) + 2NaNO_3(aq)$$

for which the net ionic equation is:

$$2Ag^+(aq) + CO_3^{2-}(aq) \rightleftharpoons Ag_2CO_3(s) \qquad [4]$$

There is a dynamic equilibrium in the saturated solution of silver carbonate between the solid silver carbonate and its constituent silver and carbonate ions as shown in Equation [4]. In all saturated solutions, a dynamic equilibrium exists between the solid and the ions in solution.

The silver carbonate precipitate can be dissolved by the addition of nitric acid. Protons, H^+, from the HNO_3 react with the carbonate ions, CO_3^{2-}, to form unstable carbonic acid.

$$2H^+(aq) + CO_3^{2-}(aq) \rightleftharpoons H_2CO_3(aq); \; H_2CO_3(aq) \longrightarrow CO_2(g) + H_2O(l)$$

Removal of carbonate ions results in the dissolution of silver carbonate by a shift to the left of the equilibrium represented by Equation [4].

To 0.5 mL (10 drops) of 0.1 M Na_2CO_3 in a large, clean test tube, add 10 drops of 0.01 M $AgNO_3$. Record your observations on your report sheet (11). **(CAUTION: *Avoid contact with nitric acid, HNO_3. If you come in contact with it, immediately wash the area with copious amounts of water. Avoid contact with the $AgNO_3$ solution as it will stain your skin purple. This stain is harmless and will eventually wear away.*)** Cautiously add 6 M HNO_3 dropwise to the test tube until you observe a change in appearance of the contents of the test tube (12). Save the contents for the next steps.

The above solution contains silver ions and nitrate ions because the Ag_2CO_3 dissolved in the nitric acid. Addition of chloride ions to this solution from HCl results in the precipitation of AgCl. The precipitated AgCl is in dynamic equilibrium with Ag^+ and Cl^- ions.

$$Ag^+(aq) + Cl^-(aq) \rightleftharpoons AgCl(s) \qquad [5]$$

This dynamic equilibrium can be disturbed by removing the Ag^+ ions, thereby forcing the equilibrium to shift to the left; as a result, the AgCl dissolves. Silver ions can be removed by the addition of NH_3 because they react with NH_3 to form $[Ag(NH_3)_2]^+$.

$$Ag^+(aq) + 2NH_3(aq) \rightleftharpoons [Ag(NH_3)_2]^+(aq) \qquad [6]$$

Because the equilibrium of Equation [6] lies much farther to the right than that of Equation [5], the AgCl will dissolve.

Adding acid to this ammoniacal solution will remove the NH_3 by forming NH_4^+ (see Equation [2]). This causes equilibrium 6 to shift to the left. The released Ag^+ will combine again with the Cl^- present to precipitate AgCl, as shown in Equation [5]. The reprecipitated AgCl can be redissolved by the addition of excess NH_3 for the same reason given previously (see Equation [6]).

To the solution you just saved, add 0.1 M HCl dropwise until you observe a change in the appearance of the contents of the test tube. Record your observations on your report sheet (13). **(CAUTION: *Concentrated* NH_3 *has a strong irritating odor; do not inhale. Do not get it on your skin. If you come in contact with it, immediately wash the area with copious amounts of water.*)** While mixing the contents of the test tube, add 15 M NH_3 dropwise until evidence of a chemical change occurs (14). Acidify the solution by the dropwise addition of 6 M HNO_3 until there is evidence of a chemical change. Record your observations on your report sheet (15). Again, while mixing, add 15 M NH_3 dropwise until there is no longer a change in the appearance of the contents of the test tube. Record your observations on your report sheet (16). Save the solution for the next step.

The equilibrium of Equation [6] can be disturbed by the addition of I^- from KI. Silver iodide will precipitate, removing Ag^+ and causing the equilibrium to shift to the left. The reason AgI will precipitate is because the equilibrium of Equation [7] lies much farther to the right than does the equilibrium of Equation [6].

$$I^-(aq) + Ag^+(aq) \rightleftharpoons AgI(s) \qquad\qquad [7]$$

To the solution from above, continue to add 0.1 M KI dropwise until you see evidence of a chemical reaction. Record your observations on your report sheet (17).

Dispose of the silver salt solution in the designated waste container.

Part III. Effect of Temperature on Equilibria

Heat about 75 mL of water to boiling in a 250 mL beaker on a ring stand. Place about 1 mL of 1.0 M $CoCl_2$ in a small test tube and place the test tube in the boiling water without spilling its contents. Compare the color of the cool cobalt solution to that of the hot solution (18).

GIVE IT SOME THOUGHT

a. When you heat the solution, what color does it turn?
b. Based on Equation [3], would heat be a product or a reactant in the equilibrium expression?
c. Based on these results, is the reaction endothermic or exothermic?

Dispose of the solution in the designated waste container.

NOTES AND CALCULATIONS

Name _____ Desk _____

Date _____ Laboratory Instructor _____

Chemical Equilibrium: Le Châtelier's Principle | 4 | Pre-lab Questions

Before beginning this experiment in the laboratory, you should be able to answer the following questions.

1. Briefly state Le Châtelier's principle.

2. Consider the following equilibrium:

$$BaSO_4(s) \rightleftharpoons Ba^{2+}(aq) + SO_4^{2-}(aq); \Delta H > 0$$

In which direction will the equilibrium shift if

a. H_2SO_4 is added? Why?

b. $BaCl_2$ is added? Why?

c. NaCl is added? Why?

d. Heat is added? Why?

3.   Consider the following equilibrium for nitrous acid, HNO_2, a weak acid:

$$HNO_2(aq) + H_2O(l) \rightleftharpoons H_3O^+(aq) + NO_2^-(aq)$$

In which direction will the equilibrium shift if

a.   NaOH is added?

b. $NaNO_2$ is added?

c.   HCl is added?

d.   The acid solution is made more dilute?

4.   Complete and balance the following equations; then write balanced net ionic equations.

a. $AgNO_3(aq) + HCl(aq) \rightleftharpoons$

b. $NH_3(aq) + HCl(aq) \rightleftharpoons$

c. $Na_2CO_3(aq) + HNO_3(aq) \rightleftharpoons$

5.   On the basis of Le Châtelier's principle, explain why Ag_2CO_3 dissolves when HNO_3 is added.

Name _____ Desk _____

Date _____ Laboratory Instructor _____

REPORT SHEET | EXPERIMENT

Chemical Equilibrium: | 4
Le Châtelier's Principle

Part I. Changes in Reactant or Product Concentrations

A. Copper and Nickel Ions
Colors:

1. $CuSO_4(aq)$ _____
2. $[Cu(NH_3)_4]^{2+}(aq)$ _____
3. After HCl addition _____

4. $NiCl_2(aq)$ _____
5. $[Ni(NH_3)_6]^{2+}(aq)$ _____
6. After HCl addition _____

Explain the effects of $NH_3(aq)$ and $HCl(aq)$ on the $CuSO_4$ solution in terms of Le Châtelier's principle.

7. What initially forms as pale blue and pale green precipitates when $NH_3(aq)$ is added to $[Cu(H_2O)_6]^{2+}$ and $[Ni(H_2O)_6]^{2+}$ solutions, respectively?

B. Cobalt Ions

8. Color of $CoCl_2(aq)$ _____
9. Color after the addition of $HCl(aq)$ _____
10. Color after the addition of H_2O _____

Account for the changes you observed for the cobalt solutions in terms of Le Châtelier's principle.

Part II. Equilibria Involving Sparingly Soluble Salts

11. _____

12. _____

    Account for your observations.

13. _____

    Account for your observations.

14. Did the precipitated AgCl dissolve? Explain.

15. What effect did the addition of HNO_3 have on the contents of the test tube? Explain.

16. What effect did the addition of NH_3 have on the contents of the test tube? Explain.

17. Explain the effect of the addition of KI.

Part III. Effect of Temperature on Equilibria

18. Color of cool $CoCl_2$ _____
    Color of hot $[CoCl_4]^{2-}$ _____
    Is the reaction exothermic? _____ Explain.

NOTES AND CALCULATIONS

Titration of
Acids and Bases

5

To become familiar with the techniques of titration, a volumetric method of analysis; to determine the amount of acid in an unknown.

OBJECTIVE

Apparatus

50 mL buret	balance
600 mL beaker	Bunsen burner and hose
500 mL Erlenmeyer flask	1 pt plastic bottle with plastic lid
250 mL Erlenmeyer flasks (3)	wash bottle
weighing bottle	buret clamp and ring stand
ring stand and ring	wire gauze

**APPARATUS
AND CHEMICALS**

Chemicals

19 *M* NaOH	phenolphthalein solution
potassium hydrogen phthalate (KHP, primary standard)	unknown acid

One of the most common and familiar reactions in chemistry is that of an acid with a base. This reaction is termed *neutralization*, and the essential feature of this process in aqueous solution is the combination of hydronium ions with hydroxide ions to form water.

DISCUSSION

$$H_3O^+(aq) + OH^-(aq) \longrightarrow 2H_2O(l)$$

In this experiment, you will use this reaction to determine accurately the concentration of a sodium hydroxide solution you have prepared. The process of determining the concentration of a solution is called *standardization*. Then you will measure the amount of acid in an unknown. To do this, using a buret, you will accurately measure, the volume of your standard base that is required to exactly neutralize the acid present in the unknown. The technique of accurately measuring the volume of a solution required to react with another reagent is termed *titration*.

An indicator solution is used to determine when an acid has exactly neutralized a base and vice versa. A suitable indicator changes colors when equivalent amounts of acid and base are present. The color change is termed the *end point* of the titration. Indicators change colors at different pH values. Phenolphthalein, for example, changes from colorless to pale pink at a pH of about 9. In slightly more acidic solutions, it is colorless, whereas in more alkaline solutions, it is deep pink.

In this experiment, your solution of NaOH will be standardized by your titrating it against a very pure sample of potassium hydrogen phthalate, $KHC_8H_4O_4$, of known mass. Potassium hydrogen phthalate (often abbreviated KHP) has one

KHP

acidic hydrogen. Its structure is shown here. It is called a primary standard and can be obtained in very pure form which is stable. It is a monoprotic acid with the acidic hydrogen bonded to oxygen and has a molar mass of 204.23 g/mol.

The balanced equation for the neutralization of KHP is given in Equation [1].

$$KHC_8H_4O_4(aq) + NaOH(aq) \longrightarrow H_2O(l) + KNaC_8H_4O_4(aq) \tag{1}$$

In the titration of the base NaOH against KHP, an equal number of moles of KHP and NaOH are present at the equivalence point. In other words, at the equivalence point

$$\text{moles NaOH} = \text{moles KHP} \tag{2}$$

The point at which stoichiometrically equivalent quantities are brought together is known as the *equivalence point* of the titration.

GIVE IT SOME THOUGHT

a. What stoichiometrically equivalent quantities are present at the equivalence point in this experiment?

b. How do these quantities relate to concentration?

Note that the equivalence point in a titration is a theoretical point. You can estimate it by observing some physical change associated with the condition of equivalence, such as the change in color of an indicator, which as stated previously, is termed the end point. The equivalence point and end point should closely correspond.

The most common way of quantifying concentrations is molarity (symbol M), which is defined as the number of moles of solute per liter of solution, or the number of millimoles of solute per milliliter of solution.

$$
\begin{aligned}
M &= \frac{\text{moles solute}}{\text{volume of solution in liters}} \\
&= \frac{10^{-3}\ \text{mole}}{10^{-3}\ \text{liter}} \\
&= \frac{\text{mmol}}{\text{mL}}
\end{aligned}
\tag{3}
$$

From Equation [3], the moles of solute (or mmol solute) are related to the molarity and the volume of the solution as follows:

$$M \times \text{liters} = \text{moles solute} \quad \text{and} \quad M \times \text{mL} = \text{mmol solute} \tag{4}$$

Thus, if you measure the volume of the base, NaOH, required to neutralize a known mass of KHP, you may be able to calculate the molarity of the NaOH solution.

EXAMPLE 5.1

Calculate the molarity of a solution that is made by dissolving 16.7 g of sodium sulfate, Na_2SO_4, in enough water to form 125 mL of solution.

SOLUTION:

$$\text{molarity} = \frac{\text{moles } Na_2SO_4}{\text{liters solution}}$$

Using the molar mass of Na_2SO_4, calculate the number of moles of Na_2SO_4.

$$\text{moles } Na_2SO_4 = (16.7 \text{ g } Na_2SO_4)\left(\frac{1 \text{ mol } Na_2SO_4}{142.04 \text{ g } Na_2SO_4}\right) = 0.118 \text{ mol } Na_2SO_4$$

Changing the volume of the solution to liters results in the following:

$$125 \text{ mL} \times (1 \text{ L}/1000 \text{ mL}) = 0.125 \text{ L}$$

Thus, the molarity is

$$\text{molarity} = \frac{0.118 \text{ mol } Na_2SO_4}{0.125 \text{ L}} = 0.941 \ M \ Na_2SO_4$$

EXAMPLE 5.2

What is the molarity of a NaOH solution if 35.75 mL is required to neutralize 1.070 g of KHP?

SOLUTION: Recall from Equation [2] that at the equivalence point, the number of moles of NaOH equals the number of moles of KHP.

$$\text{moles KHP} = (1.070 \text{ g KHP})\left(\frac{1 \text{ mol KHP}}{204.23 \text{ g KHP}}\right) = 5.240 \times 10^{-3} \text{ mol KHP}$$

Because this is the exact number of moles of NaOH contained in 35.75 mL of solution, its molarity is

$$\text{molarity} = \frac{5.240 \times 10^{-3} \text{ mol NaOH}}{0.03575 \text{ L}} = 0.1466 \ M \ \text{NaOH}$$

Once the molarity of the NaOH solution is known, the base can be used to determine the amount of KHP or any other acid present in a known mass of an impure sample. The percentage of KHP in an impure sample is

$$\% \text{ KHP} = \frac{\text{g KHP}}{\text{mass of sample}} \times 100\%$$

In this experiment, an acid–base indicator, phenolphthalein, is used to signal the end point in the titration. This indicator was chosen because its color change coincides so closely with the equivalence point.

EXAMPLE 5.3

What is the percentage of KHP in an impure sample of KHP that has a mass of 2.537 g and requires 32.77 mL of 0.1466 M NaOH to neutralize it?

SOLUTION: The number of grams of KHP in the sample must be determined first. Remember that at the equivalence point, the number of millimoles of NaOH equals the number of millimoles of KHP.

$$mmol\ NaOH = (32.77\ mL\ NaOH)(0.1466\ mmol\ NaOH/mL\ NaOH)$$
$$= 4.804\ mmol\ NaOH$$

Thus, there are 4.804 mmol of KHP in the sample, which corresponds to the following number of grams of KHP in the sample:

$$grams\ KHP = 4.804\ mmol\ KHP\left(\frac{1\ mol\ KHP}{1000\ mmol\ KHP}\right)\left(\frac{204.2\ g\ KHP}{1\ mol\ KHP}\right)$$
$$= 0.9810\ g\ KHP$$

Therefore,

$$\%\ KHP = \frac{0.9810\ g}{2.537\ g} \times 100\% = 38.67\%$$

PROCEDURE

Preparation of Approximately 0.100 *M* Sodium Hydroxide (NaOH) Heat 500 mL of distilled water to boiling in a 600 mL flask;* *after cooling under the water tap,* transfer to a 1-pt plastic bottle with a plastic lid. **(CAUTION: *Do not get any of the 19 M* NaOH *on yourself. If you do, immediately wash the area with copious amounts of water.*)** Add 3 mL of stock solution of bicarbonate-free NaOH (approximately 19 *M*) and shake vigorously for at least 1 min. The bottle should be stoppered to protect the NaOH solution from CO_2 in the air.

Preparation of a Buret for Use Clean a 50 mL buret with soap solution and a buret brush and thoroughly rinse with tap water. Then rinse with at least five 10 mL portions of distilled water. The water must run freely from the buret without leaving any drops adhering to its sides. Make sure the buret does not leak and the stopcock turns freely.

Reading a Buret All liquids, when placed in a buret, form a curved meniscus at their upper surface. In the case of water or water solutions, this meniscus is concave (Figure 5.1), and the most accurate buret readings are obtained by observing on the graduated scales the position of the lowest point on the meniscus.

To avoid parallax errors when taking readings, your eye must be level with the meniscus or use a meniscus reader. Wrap a strip of paper around the buret and hold the top edges of the strip together evenly. Adjust the strip so that the front and back edges are in line with the lowest part of the meniscus and take the reading by estimating to the nearest tenth of a marked division (0.01 mL). A simple way to do this for repeated readings on a buret is illustrated in Figure 5.1.

 GIVE IT SOME THOUGHT

When you are taking a proper reading from this buret, where should your eye level be?

---

*The water is boiled to remove carbon dioxide (CO_2), which would react with the NaOH and change its molarity. $NaOH(aq) + CO_2(g) \longrightarrow NaHCO_3(aq)$

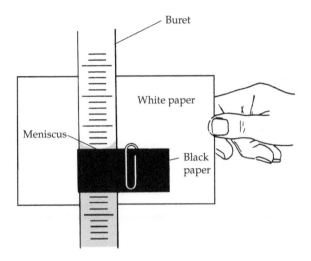

▲**FIGURE 5.1** Reading a buret.

A. Standardization of Sodium Hydroxide (NaOH) Solution

Prepare about 400 to 450 mL of CO_2-free water by boiling for about 5 min. To save time, make an additional 400 mL of CO_2-free water for Part B by boiling it now. Using a weighing bottle determine the mass of (your lab instructor will show you how to use a weighing bottle if you don't already know) triplicate samples of between 0.4 and 0.6 g each of pure potassium hydrogen phthalate (KHP) into three separate 250 mL Erlenmeyer flasks; accurately determine the mass to four significant figures.* Do not determine the mass of the flasks. Record the masses and label the three flasks so that you can distinguish among them. Add to each sample about 100 mL of distilled water that has been freed from CO_2 by boiling and warm gently with swirling until the salt is completely dissolved. Add to each flask two drops of phenolphthalein indicator solution. Cover and allow to cool before titrating the samples.

Rinse the previously cleaned buret with at least four 5 mL portions of the approximately 0.100 *M* NaOH solution that you prepared. Discard each portion into the designated receptacle. *Do not return any of the washings to the bottle.* Completely fill the buret with the solution and remove the air from the tip by dispensing some of the liquid into an empty beaker. Make sure the lower part of the meniscus is at the zero mark or slightly lower. Allow the buret to stand for at least 30 s before you read the exact position of the meniscus. Remove any hanging drop from the buret tip by touching it to the side of the beaker used for the washings. Record the initial buret reading on your report sheet.

Slowly add the NaOH solution to one of your flasks of KHP solution while gently swirling the contents of the flask, as illustrated in Figure 5.2. As the NaOH solution is added, a pink color appears where the drops of the base come in contact with the solution. This coloration disappears as you swirl the contents of the flask. As the end point is approached, the color disappears

---

*In cases where the mass of a sample is larger than 1 g, it is necessary to determine the mass only to the nearest milligram to obtain four significant figures. Buret readings can be read only to the nearest 0.02 mL, and for readings greater than 10 mL, this represents four significant figures.

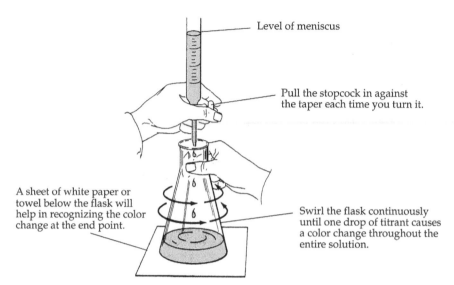

Level of meniscus

Pull the stopcock in against the taper each time you turn it.

A sheet of white paper or towel below the flask will help in recognizing the color change at the end point.

Swirl the flask continuously until one drop of titrant causes a color change throughout the entire solution.

▲**FIGURE 5.2** Titration procedure.

more slowly, at which time you should add the NaOH drop by drop. Continue swirling the flask for the entire titration. The end point is reached when one drop of the NaOH solution turns the entire solution in the flask from colorless to pink. Allow the titrated solution to stand for at least 1 min so that the buret will drain properly. Remove any hanging drop from the buret tip by touching it to the side of the flask and wash down the sides of the flask with a stream of water from the wash bottle. The solution should remain pink for about 30 s when it is swirled. Record the buret reading on your report sheet. Repeat this procedure with the other two samples. Dispose of the neutralized solutions as instructed.

From the data you obtain in the three titrations, calculate the molarity of the NaOH solution to four significant figures as in Example 5.2.

The three determinations should agree within 1.0%. If they do not, you should repeat the standardization until agreement is reached. The average of the three acceptable determinations is taken as the molarity of the NaOH. Calculate the standard deviation of your results. *Save* your standardized solution for the unknown determination.

B. Analysis of an Unknown Acid

Calculate the approximate mass of the unknown that should be taken to require about 20 mL of your standardized NaOH, assuming that your unknown sample is 75% KHP.

From a weighing bottle, determine the mass by difference of triplicate portions of the sample to four significant figures and place them in three separate 250 mL flasks. The sample size should be about the amount determined by the above computation. Dissolve the sample in 100 mL of CO_2-free distilled water (prepared by boiling and cooling) and add two drops of phenolphthalein indicator solution. Titrate with your standard NaOH solution to the faintest visible shade of pink (not red) as described previously in the standardization procedure. Calculate the percentage of KHP in the samples as in Example 5.3. For good results, the three determinations should agree within 1.0%. Your answers should have four significant figures. Compute the standard deviation of your results. Dispose of all solutions as directed.

Test your results by computing the average deviation from the mean. If one result is noticeably different from the others, perform an additional titration. If any result is more than two standard deviations from the mean, discard it and titrate another sample.

NOTES AND CALCULATIONS

Name _____ Desk _____

Date _____ Laboratory Instructor _____

Titration of Acids and Bases | 5 Pre-lab Questions

Before beginning this experiment in the laboratory, you should be able to answer the following questions.

1. Define *standardization* and state how you would go about doing it.

2. Define the term *titration.*

3. Define the term *molarity.*

4. Why do you determine a mass by difference?

5. What are equivalence points and end points? How do they differ?

6. Why should the standardized NaOH solution be kept in a stoppered bottle?

7. What is parallax? Why should you avoid it?

8.   Why is it necessary to rid the distilled water of CO_2 ?

9.   What is the molarity of a solution that contains 2.38 g of $H_2C_2O_4 \cdot 2H_2O$ in exactly 300 mL of solution?

10.   If 25.21 mL of NaOH solution is required to react completely with 0.550 g KHP, what is the molarity of the NaOH solution?

11.   The titration of an impure sample of KHP found that 36.00 mL of 0.100 M NaOH was required to react completely with 0.758 g of sample. What is the percentage of KHP in this sample?

12.   How many milliliters of 0.250 M NaOH are required to neutralize 30.4 mL of 0.146 M HCl?

REPORT SHEET | EXPERIMENT

Titration of Acids and Bases | 5

A. Standardization of Sodium Hydroxide (NaOH) Solution

	Trial 1	Trial 2	Trial 3
Mass of bottle + KHP	_____	_____	_____
Mass of bottle	_____	_____	_____
Mass of KHP used	_____	_____	_____
Final buret reading	_____	_____	_____
Initial buret reading	_____	_____	_____
mL of NaOH used	_____	_____	_____
Molarity of NaOH	_____	_____	_____

Average molarity _____ Standard deviation _____

Show your calculations for molarity and standard deviation.

B. Analysis of an Unknown Acid

	Trial 1	Trial 2	Trial 3
Mass of bottle + unknown	_____	_____	_____
Mass of bottle	_____	_____	_____
Mass of unknown used	_____	_____	_____
Final buret reading	_____	_____	_____
Initial buret reading	_____	_____	_____
mL of NaOH used	_____	_____	_____
Mass of KHP in unknown	_____	_____	_____
Percent of KHP in unknown	_____	_____	_____

Average percent of KHP _____ Standard deviation _____

Calculations of percent KHP and standard deviation (show using equations with units):

QUESTIONS

1. Write the balanced chemical equation for the reaction of KHP with NaOH.

2. Suppose your laboratory instructor inadvertently gave you a sample of KHP contaminated with NaCl to use in standardizing your NaOH. How would this affect the molarity you calculated for your NaOH solution? Justify your answer.

3. How many grams of NaOH are needed to prepare 500 mL of 0.125 M NaOH?

4. A solution of malonic acid, $H_2C_3H_2O_4$, was standardized by titration with 0.1000 M NaOH solution. If 20.76 mL of the NaOH solution is required to neutralize completely 12.95 mL of the malonic acid solution, what is the molarity of the malonic acid solution?

$$H_2C_3H_2O_4 + 2NaOH \longrightarrow Na_2C_3H_2O_4 + 2H_2O$$

5. Sodium carbonate is a reagent that may be used to standardize acids in the same way you used KHP in this experiment. In such a standardization, it was found that a 0.512 g sample of sodium carbonate required 26.30 mL of a sulfuric acid solution to reach the end point for the reaction.

$$Na_2CO_3(aq) + H_2SO_4(aq) \longrightarrow H_2O(l) + CO_2(g) + Na_2SO_4(aq)$$

What is the molarity of the H_2SO_4?

6. A solution contains 6.30×10^{-2} g of oxalic acid, $H_2C_2O_4 \cdot 2\,H_2O$, in 250 mL. What is the molarity of this solution?

Hydrolysis of Salts and pH of Buffer Solutions

To learn about the concept of hydrolysis and to gain familiarity with acid–base indicators and the behavior of buffer solutions.

Apparatus

500 mL Erlenmeyer flask	pH meter
150 mL beakers (2)	balance
10 and 100 mL graduated cylinders	1 mL pipet
test tubes (6)	Bunsen burner and hose
test-tube rack	ring stand and iron ring
wire gauze	plastic wash bottle
stirring rods (2)	

Chemicals

$NaC_2H_3O_2 \cdot 3H_2O$	dropper bottles of
$0.1\,M\ ZnCl_2$	methyl orange
$0.1\,M\ NH_4Cl$	methyl red
$0.1\,M\ KAl(SO_4)_2$	bromothymol blue
$0.1\,M\ Na_2CO_3$	phenolphthalein
$0.1\,M\ NaCl$	alizarin yellow R
$0.1\,M\ NaC_2H_3O_2$	phenol red
$6.0\,M\ HCl$	standard buffer solution (pH 4.0)
$3.0\,M\ HC_2H_3O_2$	
$6.0\,M\ NaOH$	

You expect solutions of substances such as HCl and HNO_2 to be acidic and solutions of $NaOH$ and NH_3 to be basic. However, you may be somewhat surprised to discover that aqueous solutions of some salts (for example, sodium nitrite, $NaNO_2$, and potassium acetate, $KC_2H_3O_2$) are basic, whereas others (for example, NH_4Cl and $FeCl_3$) are acidic. Recall that salts are the products formed in neutralization reactions of acids and bases. For example, when $NaOH$ and HNO_2 (nitrous acid) react, the salt $NaNO_2$ is formed.

$$NaOH(aq) + HNO_2(aq) \longrightarrow NaNO_2(aq) + H_2O(l)$$

Nearly all soluble salts are strong electrolytes and exist as ions in aqueous solutions. Many ions react with water to produce acidic or basic solutions. The reactions of ions with water are frequently called *hydrolysis reactions*. You will see that anions such as CN^- and $C_2H_3O_2^-$ that are the conjugate bases of the weak acids HCN and $HC_2H_3O_2$, respectively, react with water to form OH^- ions. Cations such as NH_4^+ and Fe^{3+} come from weak bases and react with water to form H^+ ions.

 GIVE IT SOME THOUGHT
How do you determine the acid/base strength of these cations?

A. Hydrolysis of Anions: Basic Salts

Consider the behavior of anions first. Anions of weak acids react with proton sources. When placed in water, these anions react to some extent with water to accept protons and generate OH^- ions and thus cause the solution pH values to be greater than 7. Recall that proton acceptors are Brønsted-Lowry bases. Thus, the anions of weak acids are basic in two senses: They are proton acceptors, and their aqueous solutions have pH values greater than 7. The nitrite ion, for example, reacts with water to increase the concentration of OH^- ions.

$$NO_2^-(aq) + H_2O(l) \rightleftharpoons HNO_2(aq) + OH^-(aq)$$

This reaction of the nitrite ion is similar to that of weak bases such as NH_3 with water.

$$NH_3(aq) + H_2O(l) \rightleftharpoons NH_4^+(aq) + OH^-(aq)$$

Thus, both NH_3 and NO_2^- are bases and as such have a base dissociation constant, K_b, associated with their corresponding equilibria.

According to the Brønsted-Lowry theory, the nitrite ion is the conjugate base of nitrous acid. Now consider the conjugate acid–base pair HNO_2 and NO_2^- and their behavior in water.

$$HNO_2(aq) \rightleftharpoons H^+(aq) + NO_2^-(aq) \qquad K_a = \frac{[H^+][NO_2^-]}{[HNO_2]}$$

$$NO_2^-(aq) + H_2O(l) \rightleftharpoons HNO_2(aq) + OH^-(aq) \qquad K_b = \frac{[HNO_2][OH^-]}{[NO_2^-]}$$

Multiplication of these dissociation constants yields

$$K_a \times K_b = \left(\frac{[H^+][\cancel{NO_2^-}]}{\cancel{[HNO_2]}}\right)\left(\frac{\cancel{[HNO_2]}[OH^-]}{\cancel{[NO_2^-]}}\right) = [H^+][OH^-] = K_w$$

where K_w is the ion-product constant of water.

Thus, the product of the acid-dissociation constant for an acid and the base-dissociation constant for its conjugate base is the ion-product constant for water.

$$K_a \times K_b = K_w = 1.0 \times 10^{-14} \text{ at } 25\,°C \qquad [1]$$

Knowing the K_a for a weak acid, you can easily find the K_b for the anion of the acid.

$$K_b = \frac{K_w}{K_a} \qquad [2]$$

By consulting a table of acid-dissociation constants, such as Appendix F, you can find that K_a for nitrous acid is 4.5×10^{-4}. Using this value, you can readily determine K_b for NO_2^-.

$$K_b = \frac{1.0 \times 10^{-14}}{4.5 \times 10^{-4}} = 2.2 \times 10^{-11}$$

Note that the stronger the acid the larger its K_a and that the weaker its conjugate base, the smaller its K_b. Likewise, the weaker the acid (the smaller the K_a), the stronger the conjugate base (the larger the K_b).

Anions derived from *strong acids*, such as Cl^- from HCl, do not react with water to affect the pH. Nor do Br^-, I^-, NO_3^-, SO_4^{2-}, and ClO_4^- affect the pH, for the same reason. They are spectator ions in the acid–base sense and can be described as neutral ions. Similarly, cations from strong bases, such as Na^+ from NaOH and K^+ from KOH, do not react with water to affect the pH. Hydrolysis of an ion occurs only when it can form a molecule or anion that is a weak electrolyte in the reaction with water. Strong acids and bases do not exist as molecules in dilute water solutions.

GIVE IT SOME THOUGHT

a. Do you write an equilibrium expression for a reaction involving strong acids or strong bases?

b. How does this come into play in describing these neutral cations and anions?

EXAMPLE 6.1

What is the pH of a 0.10 *M* NaClO solution if K_a for HClO is 3.0×10^{-8}?

SOLUTION: The salt NaClO exists as Na^+ and ClO^-. The Na^+ ions are spectator ions, but ClO^- ions undergo hydrolysis to form the weak acid HClO. Let x equal the equilibrium concentration of HClO (and OH^-).

$$ClO^-(aq) + H_2O(l) \rightleftharpoons HClO(aq) + OH^-(aq)$$
$$(0.10 - x)\ M \qquad\qquad x\ M \qquad\quad x\ M$$

The value of K_b for the reaction is $(1.0 \times 10^{-14}) / (3.0 \times 10^{-8}) = 3.3 \times 10^{-7}$.
Because K_b is so small, you can neglect x in comparison with 0.10; thus, $0.10 - x \approx 0.10$.

$$\frac{[HClO][OH^-]}{[ClO^-]} = K_b$$
$$\frac{x^2}{0.10} = 3.3 \times 10^{-7}$$
$$x^2 = 3.3 \times 10^{-8}$$
$$x = 1.8 \times 10^{-4}\ M$$
$$pOH = 3.74$$
$$\text{and } pH = 14 - 3.74 = 10.26$$

Anions with ionizable protons such as HCO_3^-, $H_2PO_4^-$, and HPO_4^{2-} may be acidic or basic depending upon the relative values of K_a and K_b for the ion. You will not consider such ions in this experiment.

Hydrolysis of Cations: Acidic Salts

Cations that are derived from weak bases react with water to increase the hydrogen-ion concentration; they form acidic solutions. The ammonium ion is derived from the weak base NH_3 and reacts with water as follows:

$$NH_4^+(aq) + H_2O(l) \rightleftharpoons H_3O^+(aq) + NH_3(aq)$$

This reaction is completely analogous to the dissociation of any other weak acid, such as acetic acid or nitrous acid. You can represent this acid dissociation of NH_4^+ more simply.

$$NH_4^+(aq) \rightleftharpoons NH_3(aq) + H^+(aq)$$

Here too the acid dissociation constant is related to the K_b of NH_3, which is the conjugate base of NH_4^+.

$$NH_3(aq) + H_2O(l) \rightleftharpoons NH_4^+(aq) + OH^-(aq)$$

Knowing the value of K_b for NH_3, you can readily calculate the acid dissociation constant from Equation [3].

$$K_a = \frac{K_w}{K_b} \qquad [3]$$

Cations of the alkali metals (group 1A) and the larger alkaline earth ions, Ca^{2+}, Sr^{2+}, and Ba^{2+}, do not react with water because they come from strong bases. Thus, these ions have no influence on the pH of aqueous solutions. They are merely spectator ions in acid–base reactions. Consequently, they are described as being neutral in the acid–base sense. The cations of most other metals do hydrolyze to produce acidic solutions. Metal cations are coordinated with water molecules, and it is the hydrated ion that serves as the proton donor. The following equations illustrate this behavior for the hexaaquairon (III) ion:

$$[Fe(H_2O)_6]^{3+}(aq) + H_2O(l) \rightleftharpoons [Fe(OH)(H_2O)_5]^{2+}(aq) + H_3O^+(aq) \qquad [4]$$

The coordinated water molecules are frequently omitted from such equations. For example, Equation [4] may be written as follows:

$$Fe^{3+}(aq) + H_2O(l) \rightleftharpoons Fe(OH)^{2+}(aq) + H^+(aq) \qquad [5]$$

Additional hydrolysis reactions can occur to form $Fe(OH)_2^+$ and may even lead to the precipitation of $Fe(OH)_3$. The equilibria for such cations are often complex, and not all species have been identified. However, equations such as [4] and [5] serve to illustrate the acidic character of dipositive and tripositive ions and account for most of the H^+ in these solutions.

Summary of Hydrolysis Behavior

Whether a solution of a salt will be acidic, neutral, or basic can be predicted on the basis of the strengths of the acid and base from which the salt was formed.

1. *Salt of a strong acid and a strong base*: Examples: NaCl, KBr, and $Ba(NO_3)_2$. Neither the cation nor anion hydrolyzes, and the solution has a pH of 7. It is neutral.

2. *Salt of a strong acid and a weak base*: Examples: NH_4Br, $ZnCl_2$, and $Al(NO_3)_3$. The cation hydrolyzes, forming H^+ ions, and the solution has a pH less than 7. It is acidic.

3. *Salt of a weak acid and a strong base*: Examples: $NaNO_2$, $KC_2H_3O_2$, and $Ca(OCl)_2$. The anion hydrolyzes, forming OH^- ions, and the solution has a pH greater than 7. It is basic.

4. *Salt of a weak acid and a weak base*: Examples: NH_4F, $NH_4C_2H_3O_2$, and $Zn(NO_2)_2$. Both ions hydrolyze. The pH of the solution is determined by the relative extent to which each ion hydrolyzes.

In this experiment, you will test the pH of water and of several aqueous salt solutions to determine whether these solutions are acidic, basic, or neutral. In each case, the salt solution will be 0.1 M. Knowing the concentration of the salt solution and the measured pH of each solution allows you to calculate K_a or K_b for the ion that hydrolyzes. Example 6.2 illustrates such calculations.

EXAMPLE 6.2

Calculate K_b for OBr^- assuming that a 0.10 M solution of NaOBr has a pH of 10.85.

SOLUTION: The spectator ion is Na^+. Alkali metal ions do not react with water and have no influence on pH. The ion OBr^- is the anion of a weak acid and thus reacts with water to produce OH^- ions.

$$OBr^- + H_2O \rightleftharpoons HOBr + OH^-$$

The corresponding expression for the base dissociation constant is

$$K_b = \frac{[HOBr][OH^-]}{[OBr^-]} \qquad [6]$$

If the pH is 10.85,

$$pOH = 14.00 - 10.85 = 3.15$$

and

$$[OH^-] = \text{antilog}\,(-3.15) = 7.1 \times 10^{-4} \, M$$

The concentration of HOBr that is formed along with OH^- must also be $7.1 \times 10^{-4} \, M$. The concentration of OBr^- that has not hydrolyzed is

$$[OBr^-] = 0.10 \, M - 0.00071 \, M \simeq 0.10 \, M$$

Substituting these values into Equation [6] for K_b yields

$$K_b = \frac{[7.1 \times 10^{-4}][7.1 \times 10^{-4}]}{[0.10]}$$
$$= 5.0 \times 10^{-6}$$

You will use a set of indicators to determine the pH of various salt solutions. The dark areas in Figure 6.1 denote the transition ranges for the indicators you will use.

GIVE IT SOME THOUGHT
What is the function of an indicator?

Generally, you will find the solutions tested to be more acidic than you would have predicted them to be. A major reason for this increased acidity is the occurrence of CO_2 dissolved in the solutions. CO_2 reacts with water to generate H^+.

$$CO_2(g) + H_2O(l) \rightleftharpoons H_2CO_3(aq) \rightleftharpoons H^+(aq) + HCO_3^-(aq)$$

The solubility of CO_2 is greatest in basic solutions, intermediate in neutral solutions, and least in acidic solutions. Therefore, even distilled water will be somewhat acidic unless it is boiled to remove the dissolved CO_2.

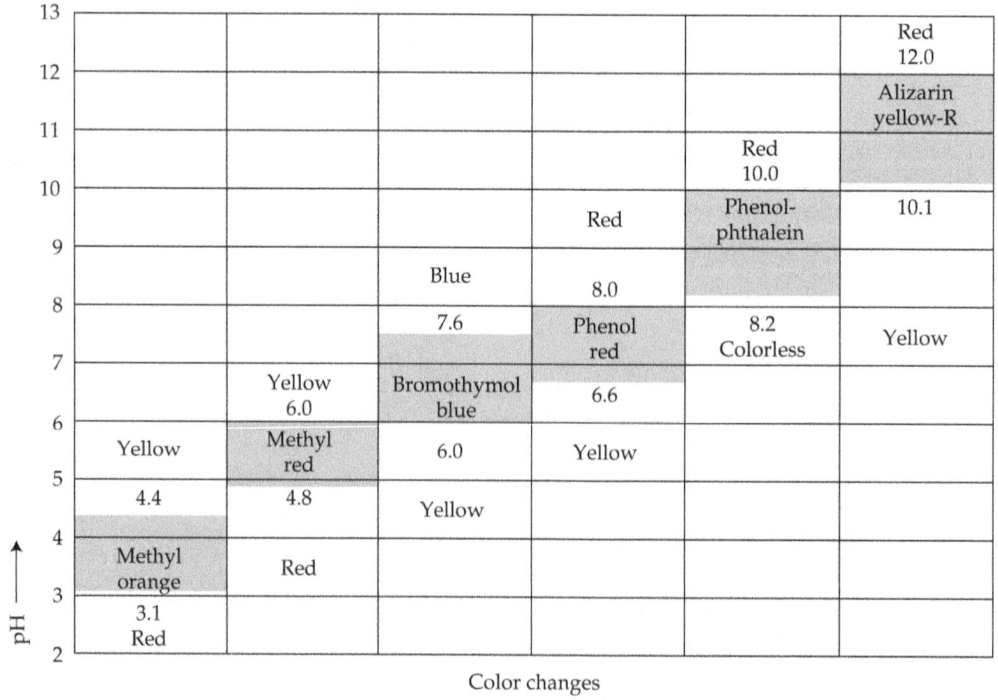

▲**FIGURE 6.1** The color behavior of indicators.

B. Buffer Solutions

Chemists, biologists, and environmental scientists frequently need to control the pH of aqueous solutions. The effects on pH caused by the addition of a small amount of a strong acid or base to water are dramatic. The addition of a mere 0.001 mole of HCl to 1 L of water causes the pH to drop instantly from 7.0 to 3.0 as the hydronium ion concentration increases from 1×10^{-7} to 1×10^{-3} mol/L. On the other hand, the addition of 0.001 mole of NaOH to 1 L of water causes the pH to increase from 7.0 to 11.0. That life could not exist without some mechanism for controlling or absorbing excess acid or base is indicated by the narrow normal range of blood pH—7.35 to 7.45.

 GIVE IT SOME THOUGHT

What is the function of a buffer?

The control of pH is often accomplished by use of *buffer solutions* (often simply called *buffers*) (Section 9.2). A buffer solution has the important property of resisting large changes in pH upon the addition of small amounts of strong acids or bases. A buffer solution must have two components—one that will react with H^+ and the other that will react with OH^-. The two components of a buffer solution are usually a weak acid and its conjugate base, such as $HC_2H_3O_2$–$C_2H_3O_2^-$ or NH_4^+–NH_3. Thus, buffers are often prepared by mixing a weak acid or a weak base with a salt of that acid or base. For example, the $HC_2H_3O_2$–$C_2H_3O_2^-$ buffer can be prepared by adding $NaC_2H_3O_2$ to a solution of $HC_2H_3O_2$; the NH_4^+–NH_3 buffer can be prepared by adding NH_4Cl to a solution of NH_3. By the appropriate choice of components and their concentrations, buffer solutions of virtually any pH can be made.

Now examine how a buffer works. Consider a buffer composed of a hypothetical weak acid HX and one of its salts MX, where M^+ could be Na^+, K^+, or another cation. The acid dissociation equilibrium in this buffer involves both the acid, HX, and its conjugate base X^-.

$$HX(aq) \rightleftharpoons H^+(aq) + X^-(aq) \qquad [1]$$

The corresponding acid dissociation constant expression is

$$K_a = \frac{[H^+][X^-]}{[HX]} \qquad [2]$$

Solving this expression for $[H^+]$, you have

$$[H^+] = K_a \frac{[HX]}{[X^-]} \qquad [3]$$

You can see from this expression that the hydrogen ion concentration (and therefore the pH) is determined by two factors: the value of K_a for the weak acid component of the buffer and the ratio of the concentrations of the weak acid and its conjugate base, $[HX]/[X^-]$.

When OH^- ions are added to the buffered solution, they react with the acid component of the buffer.

$$OH^-(aq) + HX(aq) \longrightarrow H_2O(l) + X^-(aq) \qquad [4]$$

This reaction results in a slight decrease in the [HX] and a slight increase in the $[X^-]$ as long as the amounts of HX and X^- in the buffer are large compared to the amount of the added OH^-. In that case, the ratio $[HX]/[X^-]$ doesn't change much; thus, the change in the pH is small.

When H^+ ions are added to the buffered solution, they react with the base component of the buffer.

$$H^+(aq) + X^-(aq) \longrightarrow HX(aq) \qquad [5]$$

This reaction causes a slight decrease in the $[X^-]$ and a slight increase in the [HX]. Once again, as long as the change in the ratio $[HX]/[X^-]$ is small, the change in the pH will be small.

Buffers resist changes in pH most effectively when the concentrations of the conjugate acid–base pair, HX and X^-, are about the same. From examining Equation [3], you can see that under these conditions, their ratio is close to one; thus, the $[H^+]$ is approximately equal to K_a. For this reason, you try to select a buffer whose acid form has a pK_a close to the desired pH.

With regard to pH, you take the negative logarithm of both sides of Equation [3] and obtain

$$-\log[H^+] = -\log K_a - \log\frac{[HX]}{[X^-]}$$

Because $-\log[H^+] = pH$ and $-\log[K_a] = pK_a$, you have

$$pH = pK_a - \log\frac{[HX]}{[X^-]}$$

And making use of the properties of logarithms, you have

$$pH = pK_a + \log\frac{[X^-]}{[HX]} \qquad [6]$$

In general,

$$pH = pK_a + \log\frac{[\text{conjugate base}]}{[\text{weak acid}]} \qquad [7]$$

This relationship is known as the *Henderson-Hasselbalch equation* (Section 9.2). Biochemists, biologists, and others who frequently work with buffers often use this equation to calculate the pH of buffers. What makes this equation particularly convenient is that you can usually neglect the amounts of the acid and base of the buffer that ionize because they are comparatively small. Therefore, you can use the *initial concentrations* of the acid and conjugate base components of the buffer directly in Equation [7].

EXAMPLE 6.3

What is the pH of a buffer that is 0.120 M in lactic acid, $HC_3H_5O_3$, and 0.100 M in sodium lactate, $NaC_3H_5O_3$? For lactic acid, $K_a = 1.4 \times 10^{-4}$.

SOLUTION: Because lactic acid is a weak acid, you may assume that its initial concentration is 0.120 M and that none of it has dissociated. You may also assume that the lactate ion concentration is that of the salt, sodium lactate, 0.100 M. Let x represent the concentration in mol/L of the lactic acid that dissociates. The initial and equilibrium concentrations involved in this equilibrium are as follows:

$$HC_3H_5O_3(aq) \rightleftharpoons H^+(aq) + C_3H_5O_3^-(aq)$$

Initial	0.120 M	0	0.100 M
Change	$- x\ M$	$+ x\ M$	$+ x\ M$
Equilibrium	$(0.120 - x)\ M$	$x\ M$	$(0.100 + x)\ M$

The equilibrium concentrations are governed by the equilibrium expression

$$K_a = 1.4 \times 10^{-4} = \frac{[H^+][C_3H_5O_3^-]}{[HC_3H_5O_3]} = \frac{x(0.100 + x)}{0.120 - x}$$

Because K_a is small and because of the presence of a common ion, you can expect x to be small relative to 0.120 and 0.100 M, i.e. that [initial] approximately equals [initial-x]. Thus, the equation can be simplified to give

$$1.4 \times 10^{-4} = \frac{x(0.100)}{0.120}$$

Solving for x gives a value that justifies your neglecting it.

$$x = [H^+] = \left(\frac{0.120}{0.100}\right)(1.4 \times 10^{-4}) = 1.7 \times 10^{-4}\ M$$

$$pH = -\log(1.7 \times 10^{-4}) = 3.77$$

Alternatively, you could have used the Henderson-Hasselbalch equation to calculate the pH directly.

$$pH = pK_a + \log\left(\frac{[\text{conjugate base}]}{[\text{weak acid}]}\right) = 3.85 + \log\left(\frac{0.100}{0.120}\right)$$

$$= 3.85 + (-0.08) = 3.77$$

Addition of Strong Acids or Bases to Buffers

Now consider in a quantitative way the manner in which a buffer solution responds to the addition of a strong acid or base. Consider a buffer that consists of the weak acid HX and its conjugate base X^- (from the salt NaX). When a strong acid is added to this buffer, the H^+ is consumed by the X^- to produce HX; thus, [HX] increases and $[X^-]$ decreases. Whereas when a strong base is added to the buffer, the OH^- is consumed by HX to produce X^-; in this case, [HX] decreases and $[X^-]$ increases. Basically, two steps are involved in calculating how the pH of the buffer responds to the addition of a strong acid or base. First, consider the acid–base neutralization reaction and determine its effect on [HX] and [X⁻]. Second, after performing this stoichiometric calculation, use K_a and the new concentrations of [HX] and [X⁻] to calculate the [H⁺]. This second step in the calculation is a standard equilibrium calculation. This procedure is illustrated in Example 6.4.

EXAMPLE 6.4

A buffer is made by adding 0.120 mol of $HC_3H_5O_3$ and 0.100 mol of $NaC_3H_5O_3$ to enough water to make 1.00 L of solution. The pH of the buffer is 3.77 (see Example 6.3). Calculate the pH of the solution after 0.001 mol of NaOH is added. Assume no volume change.

SOLUTION: Solving this problem involves two steps.

Stoichiometric calculation: The OH⁻ provided by the NaOH reacts with the $HC_3H_5O_3$, the weak acid component of the buffer. The following table summarizes the concentrations before and after the neutralization reaction:

$$HC_3H_5O_3(aq) + OH^-(aq) \longrightarrow H_2O(l) + C_3H_5O_3^-(aq)$$

Before reaction	0.120 M	0.001 M	–	0.100 M
Change	−0.001 M	−0.001 M	–	+ 0.001 M
After reaction	0.119 M	0.0 M	–	0.101 M

Equilibrium calculation: After neutralization, the solution contains different concentrations for the weak acid–conjugate base pair. Now consider the following proton–transfer equilibrium to determine the pH of the solution:

$$HC_3H_5C_3(aq) + H_2O(aq) \rightleftharpoons H_3O^+(aq) + C_3H_5O_3^-(aq)$$

Before reaction	0.119 M	–	0	0.101 M
Change	$- x\ M$	–	$+ x\ M$	$+ x\ M$
After reaction	$(0.119 - x)\ M$	–	$x\ M$	$(0.101 + x)\ M$

$$K_a = \frac{[H_3O^+][C_3H_5O_3^-]}{[HC_3H_5O_3]} = \frac{(x)(0.101 + x)}{0.119 - x} \approx \frac{(x)(0.101)}{0.119} \cong 1.4 \times 10^{-4}$$

$$x = [H_3O^+] = \frac{(0.119)(1.4 \times 10^{-4})}{(0.101)} = 1.65 \times 10^{-4}\ M$$

$$pH = -\log(1.65 \times 10^{-4}) = 3.78$$

Note how the buffer resists a change in its pH. The addition of 0.001 mol of NaOH to a liter of this buffer results in a change in the pH of only 0.01 units whereas the addition of the same amount of NaOH to a liter of water results in a change of pH from 7.0 to 11.0, a change of 4.0 pH units!

A. Hydrolysis of Salts

PROCEDURE   Boil approximately 450 mL of distilled water for about 10 min to expel dissolved carbon dioxide. Cover and allow the water to cool to room temperature. While the water is boiling and subsequently cooling, add about 5 mL of unboiled distilled water to each of six test tubes. Add three drops of a different indicator to each of the test tubes (one indicator per tube) and record the colors on the report sheet. From these colors and the data given in Figure 6.1, determine the pH of the unboiled water to the nearest pH unit. (Remember that its pH is likely to be below 7 because of dissolved CO_2.) Empty the contents of the test tubes and rinse the test tubes three times with about 3 mL of boiled distilled water. Then pour about 5 mL of the boiled distilled water into each of the test tubes and add three drops of each indicator (one indicator per tube) to each tube. Record the colors and determine the pH. Empty the contents of the test tubes and rinse each tube three times with about 3 mL of boiled distilled water.

Repeat the same procedure to determine the pH of each of the following solutions that are 0.1 *M*: NaCl, $NaC_2H_3O_2$, NH_4Cl, $ZnCl_2$, $KAl(SO_4)_2$, and Na_2CO_3. Use 5 mL of each of these solutions per test tube. Do not forget to rinse the test tubes with boiled distilled water when you go from one solution to the next.

GIVE IT SOME THOUGHT

Before you perform the experiment, would you predict the pH of each of these salts to be greater than 7, equal to 7, or less than 7. Why?

From the pH values you determined, calculate the hydrogen and hydroxide ion concentrations for each solution. Complete the tables on the report sheets and calculate the K_a or K_b as appropriate.

Dispose of chemicals in designated receptacles as directed.

B. pH of Buffer Solutions

1.　Preparation of Acetic Acid–Sodium Acetate Buffer

Determine the mass of about 3.5 g of $NaC_2H_3O_2 \cdot 3H_2O$ to the nearest 0.01 g, record its mass, and add it to a 150 mL beaker. Using a 10 mL graduated cylinder, measure 8.8 mL of 3.0 *M* acetic acid and add it to the beaker containing the sodium acetate. Using a graduated cylinder, measure 55.6 mL of distilled water and add it to the solution of acetic acid and sodium acetate. Assume that the volumes are additive. Stir the solution until all of the sodium acetate is dissolved. You will measure the pH of this solution using a pH meter. The operation and calibration of the pH meter are described in the next section. Calibrate the pH meter using a standard buffer with a pH of 4.0. After you have calibrated the pH meter, measure the pH of the buffer solution you have prepared and record the value. Save this buffer solution for Part 2.

GIVE IT SOME THOUGHT

Why is a solution of acetic acid and sodium acetate a candidate for a buffer solution?

Operation and Calibration of the pH Meter

1. Obtain a buffer solution of known pH.

2. Plug in the pH meter to the line current and allow at least 10 min for it to warm up. You should leave it plugged in until you are finished using it. *This does not apply to battery-operated meters.*

3. Turn the function knob on the pH meter to the standby position as directed.

4. *Prepare the electrodes.* Make certain the solution in the reference electrode extends well above the internal electrode. If it does not, ask your instructor to fill it with saturated KCl solution. Remove the rubber tip and slide down the rubber collar on the reference electrode. Thoroughly rinse the outside of the electrodes with distilled water as directed.

5. *Standardize the pH meter.* Carefully immerse the electrodes in the buffer solution contained in a small beaker. *Remember that the glass electrode is very fragile; it breaks easily!* Do not touch the bottom of the beaker with the electrodes! Turn the function knob to "read" or "pH." Turn the standardize knob until the pH meter indicates the exact pH of the buffer solution. Wait 5 s to make certain the reading remains constant. *Once you have standardized the pH meter, do not readjust the standardize knob.* Turn the function knob to standby. Carefully lift the electrodes from the buffer and rinse them with distilled water. The pH meter is now ready to use to measure pH.

2.   Effect of Acid and Base on the Buffer pH

Pour half (32 mL) of the buffer solution you prepared earlier into another 150 mL beaker. Label the two beakers 1 and 2. (**CAUTION:** *Concentrated HCl can cause severe burns. Avoid contact with it. If you come in contact with it, immediately wash the area with copious amounts of water.*) Pipet 1.0 mL of 6.0 *M* HCl into beaker 1, mix, and then measure the pH of the resultant solution and record the pH. Remember to rinse the electrodes between pH measurements. (**CAUTION:** *Sodium hydroxide can cause severe burns. Avoid contact with it. If you come in contact with it, immediately wash the area with copious amounts of water.*) Similarly, pipet 1.0 mL of 6.0 *M* NaOH into beaker 2, mix, and then measure and record the pH of the resultant solution. Calculate the pH values of the original buffer solution and the values after the additions of the HCl and NaOH. How do the measured and calculated values compare? Dispose of the chemicals in the designated receptacles.

Name _____ Desk _____

Date _____ Laboratory Instructor _____

Hydrolysis of Salts and pH of Buffer Solutions | 6 Pre-lab Questions

Before beginning this experiment in the laboratory, you should be able to answer the following questions.

1. Define Brønsted-Lowry acids and bases.

2. Which of the following ions will react with water in a hydrolysis reaction: K^+, Ba^{2+}, Cu^{2+}, Zn^{2+}, F^-, SO_3^{2-}, and Cl^-?

3. For those ions in question 2 that undergo hydrolysis, write net ionic equations for the hydrolysis reaction.

4. The K_a for HCN is 4.9×10^{-10}. What is the value of K_b for CN^-?

5. What are the conjugate base and conjugate acid of $H_2PO_4^-$?

6. From what acid and what base were the following salts made: K_2SO_4, NH_4Cl, and $Ca(NO_3)_2$?

7.   Define the term *salt.*

8.   Tell whether 0.1 *M* solutions of the following salts would be acidic, neutral, or basic: $BaCl_2$, $CuSO_4$, $(NH_4)_2SO_4$, $ZnCl_2$, and NaCN.

9.   If the pH of a solution is 6, what are the hydrogen and hydroxide ion concentrations?

10.   The pH of a 0.1 *M* MCl (M^+ is an unknown cation) was found to be 4.7. Write a net ionic equation for the hydrolysis of M^+ and its corresponding equilibrium expression K_b. Calculate the value of K_b.

11.   What is the pH of a solution that is 0.20 *M* $HC_2H_3O_2$ and 0.40 *M* $NaC_2H_3O_2$? K_a for acetic acid is 1.8×10^{-5}.

Name _____ Desk _____

Date _____ Laboratory Instructor _____

Hydrolysis of Salts and pH of Buffer Solutions

6

A. Hydrolysis of Salts

Solution	Ion expected to hydrolyze (if any)	Spectator ion(s) (if any)
0.1 M NaCl	_____	_____
0.1 M Na$_2$CO$_3$	_____	_____
0.1 M NaC$_2$H$_3$O$_2$	_____	_____
0.1 M NH$_4$Cl	_____	_____
0.1 M ZnCl$_2$	_____	_____
0.1 M KAl(SO$_4$)$_2$	_____	_____

Indicator Color*

Solution	Methyl orange	Methyl red	Bromo-thymol blue	Phenol red	Phenol-phtha-lein	Alizarin yellow R	pH	$[H^+]$ M	$[OH^-]$ M
H$_2$O (unboiled)									
H$_2$O (boiled)									
NaCl									
NaC$_2$H$_3$O$_2$									
NH$_4$Cl									
ZnCl$_2$									
KAl(SO$_4$)$_2$									
Na$_2$CO$_3$									

*Color key: org = orange; —— = colorless; yell = yellow.

CALCULATIONS

Solution	Net-ionic equation for hydrolysis	Expression for equilibrium constant (K_a or K_b)	Value of (K_a or K_b)
$NaC_2H_3O_2$	_____	_____	_____
Na_2CO_3	_____	_____	_____
NH_4Cl	_____	_____	_____
$ZnCl_2$	_____	_____	_____
$KAl(SO_4)_2$	_____	_____	_____

QUESTIONS

1. Using the K_a's for $HC_2H_3O_2$ and HCO_3^-, calculate the K_b's for the $C_2H_3O_2^-$ and CO_3^{2-} ions. Compare these values with those calculated from your measured pH's.

2. Using K_b for NH_3 (from Appendix G), calculate K_a for the NH_4^+ ion. Compare this value with that calculated from your measured pH's.

3. How should the pH of a 0.1 M solution of $NaC_2H_3O_2$ compare with that of a 0.1 M solution of $KC_2H_3O_2$? Explain briefly.

4. What is the greatest source of error in this experiment? How could you minimize this source of error?

B. pH of Buffer Solutions

Mass of $NaC_2H_3O_2 \cdot 3H_2O$ (FW $= 136$ g/mol)   _____

pH of original buffer solution   _____

pH of buffer + HCl   _____

pH buffer + NaOH   _____

Calculate pH of original buffer (show calculations)   _____

Calculate pH of buffer + HCl (show calculations)   _____

Calculate pH of buffer + NaOH (show calculations)   _____

NOTES AND CALCULATIONS

Determination of the Dissociation Constant of a Weak Acid

OBJECTIVE

To become familiar with the operation of a pH meter and use pH to determine the magnitude of the equilibrium constant of a weak acid.

APPARATUS AND CHEMICALS

Apparatus

pH meter with electrodes
balance
150 mL beakers (4)
buret
1 pt plastic bottle with plastic lid
Bunsen burner and hose
wire gauze

600 mL Erlenmeyer flask
250 mL Erlenmeyer flasks (3)
25 mL pipet and pipet bulb
buret clamp and ring stand
weighing bottle
ring stand and ring
wash bottle

Chemicals

potassium hydrogen phthalate (KHP)
standard buffer solution
unknown solution of a weak acid
  (~ 0.1 M)

0.1 M NaOH or 19 M NaOH
phenolphthalein indicator
  solution
Buffer solution pH = 4.0

DISCUSSION

Acid–Base Equilibria

According to the Brønsted-Lowry acid–base theory, the strength of an acid is related to its ability to donate protons. All acid–base reactions are then competitions between bases of various strengths for these protons. For example, the strong acid HCl reacts with water according to Equation [1].

$$HCl(aq) + H_2O(l) \longrightarrow H_3O^+(aq) + Cl^-(aq) \qquad [1]$$

This acid is a strong acid and is completely dissociated—in other words, 100% dissociated—in dilute aqueous solution. Consequently, the $[H_3O^+]$ concentration of 0.1 M HCl is 0.1 M.

By contrast, acetic acid, CH_3COOH (abbreviated HOAc), is a weak acid and is only slightly dissociated to form hydronium and acetate (abbreviated OAc^-) ions, as shown in Equation [2],

$$H_2O(l) + HOAc(aq) \rightleftharpoons H_3O^+(aq) + OAc^-(aq) \qquad [2]$$

Therefore, its acid dissociation constant, as shown by Equation [3], is small.

$$K_a = \frac{[H_3O^+][OAc^-]}{[HOAc]} = 1.8 \times 10^{-5} \qquad [3]$$

Acetic acid only partially dissociates in aqueous solution, and an appreciable quantity of undissociated acetic acid remains in solution.

For the general weak acid HA in aqueous solution, the dissociation reaction and dissociation constant expression are

$$HA(aq) + H_2O(l) \rightleftharpoons H_3O^+(aq) + A^-(aq) \tag{4}$$

$$K_a = \frac{[H_3O^+][A^-]}{[HA]} \tag{5}$$

Recall that pH is defined as

$$-\log[H_3O^+] = pH \tag{6}$$

Solving Equation [5] for $[H_3O^+]$ and substituting this quantity into Equation [6] yields

$$[H_3O^+] = K_a \frac{[HA]}{[A^-]} \tag{7}$$

$$-\log[H_3O^+] = -\log K_a - \log\frac{[HA]}{[A^-]} \tag{8}$$

$$pH = pK_a - \log\frac{[HA]}{[A^-]} \tag{9}$$

where $pK_a = -\log K_a$

If you titrate the weak acid HA with a base, there will be a point in the titration at which the number of moles of base added is half the number of moles of acid initially present. This is the point at which 50% of the acid has been titrated to produce A^- and 50% remains as HA. At this point, $[HA] = [A^-]$, the ratio $[HA]/[A^-] = 1$, and $\log [HA]/[A^-] = 0$. Hence, at this point in a titration (that is, at half the equivalence point) Equation [9] becomes

$$pH = pK_a \tag{10}$$

By titrating a weak acid with a strong base and recording the pH versus the volume of base added, you can determine the ionization constant of the weak acid. This is accomplished by using the titration curve based on the titration data, as explained in the following paragraph.

From the titration curve (Figure 7.1), you can see that at the point denoted as half the equivalence point, where $[HA] = [A^-]$, the pH is 4.3. Thus, from Equation [10], at this point, $pH = pK_a$, or

$$pK_a = 4.3$$
$$-\log K_a = 4.3$$
$$\log K_a = -4.3$$
$$K_a = 5 \times 10^{-5}$$

(Your instructor will show you a graphical method for locating the equivalence point on your titration curves.)

Operation of the pH Meter

To measure the pH during the course of the titration, you will use an electronic instrument called a pH meter. This device consists of a meter and an electrode assembly, as illustrated in Figure 7.2. You may have a digital pH meter rather than the analog one illustrated here.

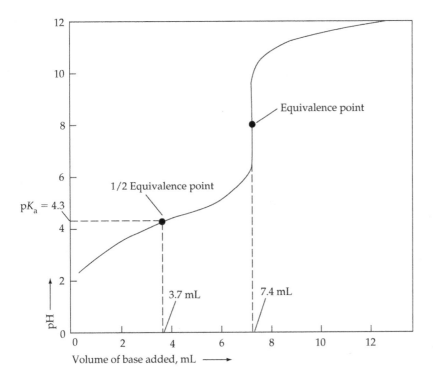

▲**FIGURE 7.1** Exemplary titration curve for the titration of a weak acid HA with a strong base.

The main differences among pH meters involve the positions of the control knobs and the types of electrodes and electrode-mounting devices. The measurement of pH requires two electrodes: a sensing electrode that is sensitive to H_3O^+ concentrations and a reference electrode or a combination electrode. The two electrodes are necessary because the pH meter is really just a voltmeter that measures the electrical potential of a solution. Typical sensing and reference electrodes are illustrated in Figure 7.3.

The reference electrode is an electrode that develops a known potential that is essentially independent of the contents of the solution into which it is

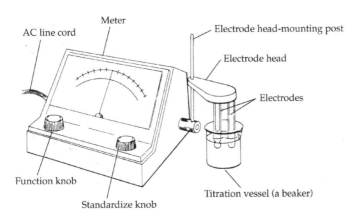

▲**FIGURE 7.2** An analog pH meter.

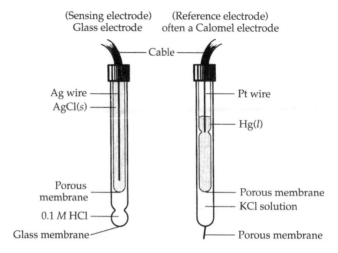

▲**FIGURE 7.3** A typical sensing and reference electrode.

placed. The glass electrode is sensitive to the H_3O^+ concentration of the solution into which it is placed; its potential is a function of $[H_3O^+]$. It operates by transport of H_3O^+ ions through the glass membrane. This can be described more precisely, but for purposes here, it is sufficient for you to understand that two electrodes are required. These two electrodes are sometimes combined into an electrode called a combination electrode which appears to be a single electrode. However, the combination electrode does contain both a reference and a sensing electrode.

Preliminary Operations with the pH Meter

1.   Obtain a buffer solution of known pH.

   GIVE IT SOME THOUGHT

   What is the function of a buffer solution?

2.   Plug in the pH meter to line current and allow at least 10 min for warm-up. You should leave the meter plugged in until you are finished with it. *This does not apply to battery-operated meters.*

3.   Turn the function knob on the pH meter to the standby position.

4.   *Prepare the electrodes.* Make certain the solution in the reference electrode extends well above the internal electrode. If it does not, ask your instructor to fill it with saturated KCl solution. Remove the rubber tip and slide down the rubber collar on the reference electrode. Rinse the outside of the electrodes thoroughly with distilled water.

5.   *Standardize the pH meter.* Carefully immerse the electrodes in the buffer solution contained in a small beaker. *Remember that the glass electrode is very fragile; it breaks easily! Do not* touch the bottom of the beaker with the electrodes! Turn the function knob to "read" or "pH." Turn the standardize knob until the pH meter indicates the exact pH of the buffer solution. Wait 5 s to make sure the reading remains constant. *Once you*

have standardized the pH meter, don't readjust the standardize knob. Turn the function knob to standby. Carefully lift the electrodes from the buffer and rinse them with distilled water. The pH meter is now ready to use to measure pH.

RECORD ALL DATA DIRECTLY ON THE REPORT SHEETS.

PROCEDURE

A. Preparation of Approximately 0.100 *M* Sodium Hydroxide (NaOH)

Heat 500 mL of distilled water to boiling in a 600 mL flask*; *after cooling under the water tap*, transfer it to a 1 pt plastic bottle with a plastic lid. **(CAUTION: *Concentrated* NaOH *can cause severe burns. If you come in contact with it, immediately wash the area with copious amounts of water.*)** Add 3 mL of stock solution of carbonate-free NaOH (approximately 19 *M*) and shake vigorously for at least 1 min.

Preparation of a Buret for Use Clean a 50 mL buret with soap solution and a buret brush and thoroughly rinse with tap water. Then rinse with at least five 10 mL portions of distilled water. The water must run freely from the buret without any drops adhering to the sides. Make sure the buret does not leak and the stopcock turns freely.

Reading a Buret All liquids, when placed in a buret, form a curved meniscus at their upper surface. In the case of water and water solutions, this meniscus is concave (Figure 7.4), and the most accurate buret readings are obtained by observing the position of the lowest point on the meniscus on the graduated scales.

 GIVE IT SOME THOUGHT
  a. What is a parallax error?
  b. Where should your eye level be when you are reading the buret?

To avoid parallax errors when taking readings, your eye must be on a level with the meniscus or use a meniscus reader. Wrap a strip of paper around the buret and hold the top edges of the strip together, making sure they are even. Adjust the strip so that the front and back edges are in line with the lowest part of the meniscus and take the reading by estimating to the nearest tenth of a marked division (0.01 mL). A simple way to do this for repeated readings on a buret is illustrated in Figure 7.4.

---

*The water is boiled to remove carbon dioxide (CO_2), which would react with the NaOH and change its molarity.

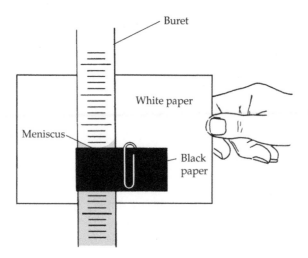

▲**FIGURE 7.4** Reading a buret.

B. Standardization of Sodium Hydroxide (NaOH) Solution

Prepare about 400 to 450 mL of CO_2-free water by boiling for about 5 min. Determine the mass of a weighing bottle (your lab instructor will show you how to use a weighing bottle if you don't already know) of triplicate samples of between 0.4 and 0.6 g each of pure potassium hydrogen phthalate (KHP, $KHC_8H_4O_4$, molar mass 204.22 g/mol) in three separate 250 mL Erlenmeyer flasks; accurately determine the mass to four significant figures.* Do not determine the mass of the flasks. Record the masses and label the three flasks so that you can distinguish among them. Add to each sample about 100 mL of distilled water that has been freed from CO_2 by boiling and warm gently by swirling until the salt is completely dissolved. Cover and allow to cool before titrating the samples. Add to each flask two drops of phenolphthalein indicator solution.

Rinse the previously cleaned buret with at least four 5 mL portions of the approximately 0.100 M NaOH solution that you prepared. Discard each portion into the designated receptacle. *Do not return any of the washings to the bottle.* Completely fill the buret with the solution and remove the air from the tip by dispensing some of the liquid into an empty beaker. Make sure the lower part of the meniscus is at the zero mark or slightly lower. Remove any hanging drop from the buret tip by touching it to the side of the beaker used for the washings. Allow the buret to stand for at least 30 s before you read the exact position of the meniscus. Record the initial buret reading on your report sheet.

Slowly add the NaOH solution to one of your flasks of KHP solution while gently swirling the contents of the flask, as illustrated in Figure 7.5. As the NaOH solution is added, a pink color appears where the drops of the base come in contact with the solution. This coloration disappears as you swirl the contents of the flask. As the end point is approached, the color disappears more slowly, at which time you should add the NaOH drop by drop. Continue

---

*In cases where the mass of a sample is larger than 1 g, it is necessary to determine the mass only to the nearest milligram to obtain four significant figures. Buret readings can be read only to the nearest 0.02 mL, and for readings greater than 10 mL, this represents four significant figures.

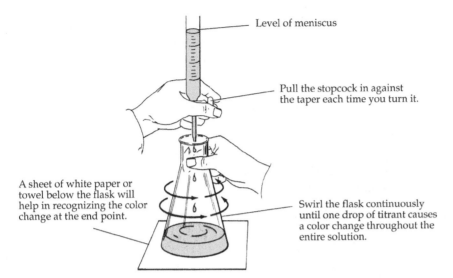

Level of meniscus

Pull the stopcock in against
the taper each time you turn it.

A sheet of white paper or
towel below the flask will
help in recognizing the color
change at the end point.

Swirl the flask continuously
until one drop of titrant causes
a color change throughout the
entire solution.

▲ **FIGURE 7.5** Titration procedure.

swirling the flask for the entire titration. The end point is reached when one drop of the NaOH solution turns the entire solution in the flask from colorless to pink that persists for at least 30 s. The solution should remain pink when it is swirled. Remove any hanging drop from the buret tip by touching it to the side of the flask and wash down the sides of the flask with a stream of water from the wash bottle. Allow the titrated solution to stand for at least 1 min so that the buret will drain properly. Record the buret reading on your report sheet. Repeat this procedure with the other two samples.

 GIVE IT SOME THOUGHT

What shade of pink indicates the end point?

From the data you obtain in the three titrations, calculate the molarity of the NaOH solution to four significant figures.

The three determinations should agree within 1.0%. If they do not, repeat the standardization until agreement is reached. The average of the three acceptable determinations is taken as the molarity of the NaOH. Calculate the standard deviation of your results. *Save* your standardized solution for determining the pK_a of the unknown acid.

C. Determination of pK_a of Unknown Acid

With the aid of a pipet bulb, pipet a 25 mL aliquot of your unknown acid solution into a 70 mL beaker and carefully immerse the previously rinsed electrodes in this solution. Measure the pH of this solution by turning the function knob to "read" or "pH." Record the pH on the report sheet. Begin your titration, under constant mixing, by adding 1 mL of your standardized base from a buret and record the volume of titrant and pH. Repeat with successive additions of 1 mL of base until you approach the end point; then add 0.1 mL increments of base and record the pH and milliliters of NaOH added. After the rapid rise in pH is completed, the base can be added again in 1 mL increments. When the pH no longer changes upon addition of NaOH, your titration is complete. From these data, plot a titration curve of pH versus mL titrant added. Repeat the titration with two more 25 mL aliquots of your unknown acid and plot the titration curves. From these curves calculate the acid-dissociation constant. You may be able to save time if the first titration is run rapidly with larger-volume increments of the titrant to locate an approximate equivalence point; then the second and third titrations may be run with the small increments indicated previously. Turn the function knob to standby; rinse the electrodes with distilled water; and wipe them with a clean, dry tissue. Return them to the appropriate storage solution.

GIVE IT SOME THOUGHT

a. At what point in the procedure do you have to be extremely careful?

b. What can you do to save time?

D. Concentration of Unknown Acid

Using the volume of base at the equivalence point, its molarity, and the fact that you used 25.00 mL of acid, calculate the concentration of the unknown acid and record this on the report sheet.

GIVE IT SOME THOUGHT

Before you perform any calculations, think about the following: Based on the volume and the concentration of the standardized base, what do you expect the concentration of your unknown acid to be?

Determination of the Dissociation Constant of a Weak Acid | 7 Pre-lab Questions

Before beginning this experiment in the laboratory, you should be able to answer the following questions.

1. Define Brønsted-Lowry acids and bases.

2. Differentiate between the dissociation constant and equilibrium constant for the dissociation of a weak acid, HA, in aqueous solution.

3. Why isn't the pH at the equivalence point always equal to 7 in a neutralization titration? When is it 7?

4. What is the pK_a of an acid whose K_a is 6.5×10^{-6}?

5. Why must two electrodes be used to make an electrical measurement such as pH?

6. What is a buffer solution?

7. The pH at one-half the equivalence point in an acid–base titration was found to be 5.67. What is the value of K_a for this unknown acid?

8. If 30.15 mL of 0.0995 M NaOH is required to neutralize 0.279 g of an unknown acid, HA, what is the molar mass of the unknown acid?

9. Assuming that K_a is 1.85×10^{-5} for acetic acid, calculate the pH at one-half the equivalence point and at the equivalence point for a titration of 50 mL of 0.100 M acetic acid with 0.100 M NaOH.

Name _____ Desk _____

Date _____ Laboratory Instructor _____

REPORT SHEET | EXPERIMENT

Determination of the Dissociation Constant of a Weak Acid

7

B. Standardization of Sodium Hydroxide (NaOH) Solution

	Trial 1	*Trial 2*	*Trial 3*
Mass of bottle + KHP	_____	_____	_____
Mass of bottle	_____	_____	_____
Mass of KHP used	_____	_____	_____
Final buret reading	_____	_____	_____
Initial buret reading	_____	_____	_____
mL of NaOH used	_____	_____	_____
Molarity of NaOH	_____	_____	_____

Average molarity (show calculations and standard deviation) _____

Standard deviation (see Experiment 8) _____

C. Determination of pK_a of Unknown Acid

First determination		*Second determination*		*Third determination*	
mL NaOH	*pH*	*mL NaOH*	*pH*	*mL NaOH*	*pH*
——	——	——	——	——	——
——	——	——	——	——	——
——	——	——	——	——	——
——	——	——	——	——	——
——	——	——	——	——	——
——	——	——	——	——	——
——	——	——	——	——	——
——	——	——	——	——	——
——	——	——	——	——	——
——	——	——	——	——	——
——	——	——	——	——	——
——	——	——	——	——	——
——	——	——	——	——	——
——	——	——	——	——	——
——	——	——	——	——	——
——	——	——	——	——	——
——	——	——	——	——	——
——	——	——	——	——	——
——	——	——	——	——	——
——	——	——	——	——	——
——	——	——	——	——	——
——	——	——	——	——	——
——	——	——	——	——	——
——	——	——	——	——	——
——	——	——	——	——	——
——	——	——	——	——	——
——	——	——	——	——	——
——	——	——	——	——	——
——	——	——	——	——	——
——	——	——	——	——	——

Volume at equivalence point   _____   _____   _____
Volume at one-half equivalence point   _____   _____   _____

pK_a _____   pK_a _____   pK_a _____

K_a _____ K_a _____ K_a _____

Average K_a (show calculations) _____   Standard deviation of K_a _____

D. Concentration of Unknown Acid

	Trial 1	Trial 2	Trial 3
Volume of unknown acid	_____	_____	_____
Average molarity of NaOH from above	_____	_____	_____
mL of NaOH at equivalence point	_____	_____	_____
Molarity of unknown acid	_____	_____	_____

Average molarity (show calculations) _____   Standard deviation _____

QUESTIONS

1. What are the largest sources of error in this experiment?

2. What is the pH of the solution obtained by mixing 30.00 mL of 0.250 M HCl and 30.00 mL of 0.125 M NaOH? We assume additive volumes.

3. What is the pH of a solution that is 0.75 M in sodium acetate and 0.50 M in acetic acid? (K_a for acetic acid is 1.8×10^{-5}.)

4. Calculate the pH of a solution prepared by mixing 15.0 mL of 0.10 M NaOH and 30.0 mL of 0.10 M benzoic acid solution. (Benzoic acid is monoprotic; its dissociation constant is 6.3×10^{-5}.) Assume additive volumes.

5. K_a for hypochlorous acid, HClO, is 3.0×10^{-8}. Calculate the pH after 10.0, 20.0, 30.0, and 40.0 mL of 0.100 M NaOH have been added to 40.0 mL of 0.100 M HClO.

Titration curve

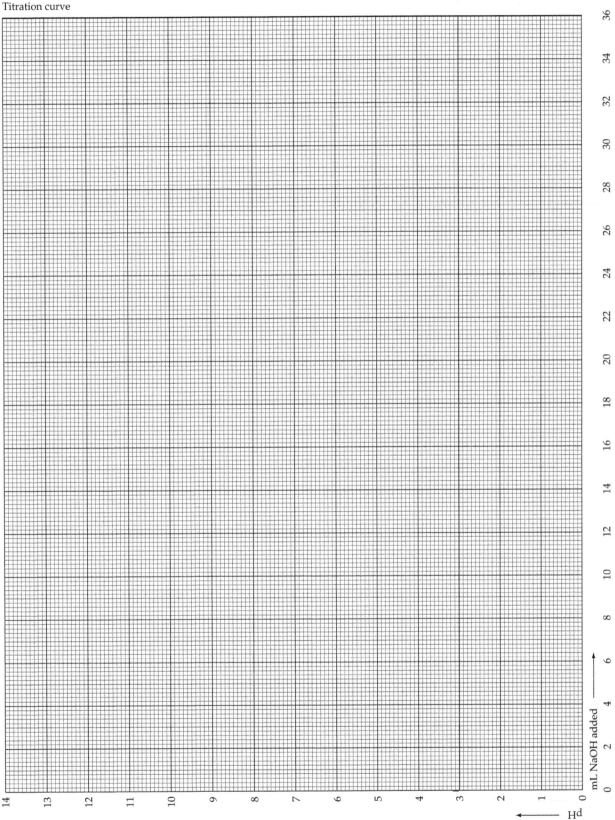

mL NaOH added

pH

Titration curve

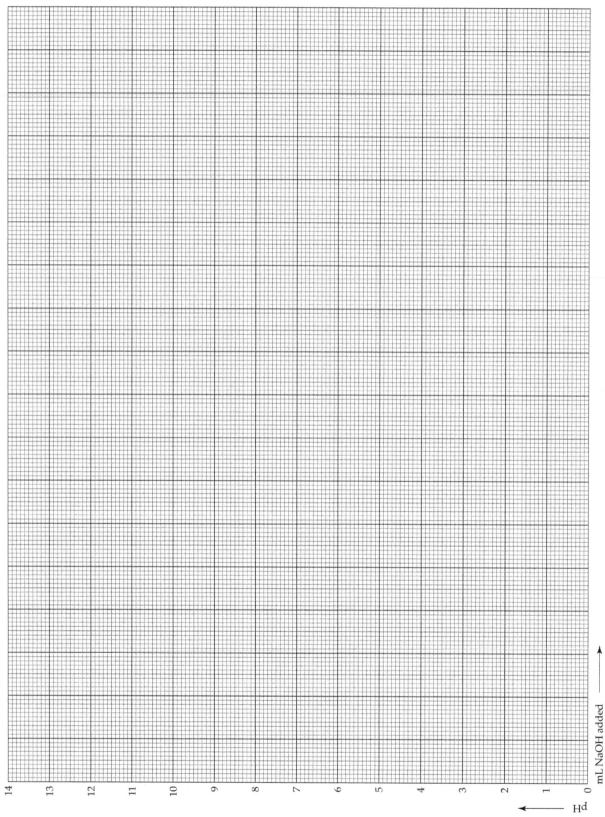

pH

mL NaOH added

Titration curve

mL NaOH added ⟶

pH

Determination of the Solubility-Product Constant for a Sparingly Soluble Salt

To become familiar with equilibria involving sparingly soluble substances by determining the value of the solubility-product constant for a sparingly soluble salt.

OBJECTIVE

APPARATUS AND CHEMICALS

Apparatus

spectrophotometer and cuvettes
5 mL pipets (2)
75 mm test tubes (3)
150 mm test tubes (3)
No. 1 corks (3)

100 mL volumetric flasks (4)
buret
centrifuge
ring stand and buret clamp

Chemicals

0.0024 M K_2CrO_4
0.25 M $NaNO_3$

0.0040 M $AgNO_3$
disposable gloves

DISCUSSION

Inorganic substances may be broadly classified into three different categories: acids, bases, and salts. According to the Brønsted-Lowry theory, acids are proton donors and bases are proton acceptors. When an acid reacts with a base in aqueous solution, the products are a salt and water, as illustrated by the following reaction of H_2SO_4 and $Ba(OH)_2$:

$$H_2SO_4\,(aq) + Ba(OH)_2\,(aq) \longrightarrow BaSO_4\,(s) + 2H_2O(l) \qquad [1]$$

With but a few exceptions, nearly all common salts are strong electrolytes. The solubilities of salts span a broad spectrum, ranging from slightly or sparingly soluble to very soluble. This experiment is concerned with heterogeneous equilibria of slightly soluble salts. For a true equilibrium to exist between a solid and a solution, the solution must be saturated. Barium sulfate is a slightly soluble salt, and in a saturated solution, this equilibrium may be represented as follows:

$$BaSO_4(s) \rightleftharpoons Ba^{2+}(aq) + SO_4^{2-}(aq) \qquad [2]$$

The equilibrium constant expression for Equation [2] is

$$K_c = \frac{[Ba^{2+}][SO_4^{2-}]}{[BaSO_4]} \qquad [3]$$

The terms in the numerator refer to the molar concentration of ions in solution. The term in the denominator refers to the "concentration" of solid $BaSO_4$.

Because the concentration of a pure solid is a constant, $[BaSO_4]$ can be combined with K_c to give a new equilibrium constant, K_{sp}, which is called the solubility-product constant ($\mathscr{O}$ Section 9.4).

$$K_{sp} = K_c[BaSO_4] = [Ba^{2+}][SO_4^{2-}]$$

At a given temperature, the value of K_{sp} is a constant. The solubility-product constant for a sparingly soluble salt can be easily calculated by determining the solubility of the substance in water. Suppose, for example, that you determined that 2.42×10^{-4} g of $BaSO_4$ dissolves in 100 mL of water. The molar solubility of this solution (that is, the molarity of the solution) is

$$\left(\frac{2.42\times10^{-4}\text{ g }BaSO_4}{100\text{ mL}}\right)\left(\frac{1000\text{ mL}}{\text{liter}}\right)\left(\frac{1\text{ mol }BaSO_4}{233.4\text{ g }BaSO_4}\right) = 1.04\times10^{-5}\ M$$

You can see from Equation [2] that for each mole of $BaSO_4$ that dissolves, one mole of Ba^{2+} and one mole of SO_4^{2-} are formed. It follows, therefore, that

$$\text{solubility of }BaSO_4\text{ in moles/liter} = [Ba^{2+}]$$
$$= [SO_4^{2-}]$$
$$= 1.04\times10^{-5}\ M$$

and

$$K_{sp} = [Ba^{2+}][SO_4^{2-}]$$
$$= [1.04\times10^{-5}][1.04\times10^{-5}]$$
$$= 1.08\times10^{-10}$$

In a saturated solution, the product of the molar concentrations of Ba^{2+} and SO_4^{2-} cannot exceed 1.08×10^{-10}. If the ion product $[Ba^{2+}][SO_4^{2-}]$ exceeds 1.08×10^{-10}, precipitation of $BaSO_4$ would occur until this product is reduced to the value of K_{sp}. Or if a solution of Na_2SO_4 is added to a solution of $Ba(NO_3)_2$, $BaSO_4$ would precipitate if the ion product $[Ba^{2+}][SO_4^{2-}]$ is greater than K_{sp}.

Similarly, if you determine that the solubility of Ag_2CO_3 is 3.49×10^{-3} g/100 mL, you could calculate the solubility-product constant for Ag_2CO_3 as follows. The solubility equilibrium involved is

$$Ag_2CO_3(s) \rightleftharpoons 2Ag^+(aq) + CO_3^{2-}(aq) \qquad [4]$$

and the corresponding solubility-product expression is

$$K_{sp} = [Ag^+]^2[CO_3^{2-}]$$

The rule for writing the solubility-product expression states that K_{sp} is equal to the product of the concentration of the ions involved in the equilibrium, each raised to the power of its coefficient in the equilibrium equation.

The solubility of Ag_2CO_3 in moles per liter is

$$\left(\frac{3.49\times10^{-3}\text{ g }Ag_2CO_3}{100\text{ mL}}\right)\left(\frac{1000\text{ mL}}{\text{liter}}\right)\left(\frac{1\text{ mol }Ag_2CO_3}{275.8\text{ g }Ag_2CO_3}\right)=1.27\times10^{-4}\ M$$

so that

$$[CO_3^{2-}]=1.27\times10^{-4}\ M\quad\text{(from Equation [4])}$$

and

$$[Ag^+]=2(1.27\times10^{-4})$$
$$=2.54\times10^{-4}\ M\quad\text{(based on the stoichiometry of Equation [4])}$$
$$K_{sp}=[Ag^+]^2[CO_3^{2-}]$$
$$=[2.54\times10^{-4}]^2[1.27\times10^{-4}]$$
$$=8.19\times10^{-12}$$

To determine the solubility of Ag_2CrO_4, you will first prepare it by the reaction of $AgNO_3$ with K_2CrO_4:

$$2AgNO_3(aq)+K_2CrO_4(aq)\rightleftharpoons Ag_2CrO_4(s)+2KNO_3(aq)$$

If a solution of $AgNO_3$ is added to a solution of K_2CrO_4, precipitation will occur when the ion product $[Ag^+]^2[CrO_4^{2-}]$ numerically exceeds the value of K_{sp}; if it doesn't exceed that value, no precipitation will occur (Section 9.6).

EXAMPLE 8.1

If the K_{sp} for PbI_2 is 7.1×10^{-9}, will precipitation of PbI_2 occur when 10 mL of $1.0\times10^{-4}M$ $Pb(NO_3)_2$ is mixed with 10 mL of $1.0\times10^{-3}\ M$ KI? Assume additive volumes.

SOLUTION:

$$PbI_2(s)\rightleftharpoons Pb^{2+}(aq)+2I^-(aq)$$
$$K_{sp}=[Pb^{2+}][I^-]^2=7.1\times10^{-9}$$

Precipitation will occur if the reaction quotient Q is greater than K_{sp} (that is if $Q=[Pb^{2+}][I^-]^2>7.1\times10^{-9}$).

$$[Pb^{2+}]=\left(\frac{10\text{ mL}}{20\text{ mL}}\right)(1.0\times10^{-4}\ M)$$
$$=5.0\times10^{-5}M$$
$$[I^-]=\left(\frac{10\text{ mL}}{20\text{ mL}}\right)(1.0\times10^{-3}M)$$
$$=5.0\times10^{-4}\ M$$
$$[Pb^{2+}][I^-]^2=[5.0\times10^{-5}][5.0\times10^{-4}]^2$$
$$=125\times10^{-13}$$
$$=1.3\times10^{-11}$$

Because $1.3 \times 10^{-11} < 7.1 \times 10^{-9}$, no precipitation will occur. However, if 10 mL of 1.0×10^{-2} M $Pb(NO_3)_2$ is added to 10 mL of 2.0×10^{-2} M KI,

$$[Pb^{2+}] = \left(\frac{10 \text{ mL}}{20 \text{ mL}}\right)(1.0 \times 10^{-3} M)$$

$$= 5.0 \times 10^{-3} \ M$$

$$[I^{-}] = \left(\frac{10 \text{ mL}}{20 \text{ mL}}\right)(2.0 \times 10^{-2})$$

$$= 1.0 \times 10^{-2} \ M$$

and

$$[Pb^{2+}][I^{-}]^2 = [5.0 \times 10^{-3}][1.0 \times 10^{-2}]^2 = 5.0 \times 10^{-7}$$

Because $5.0 \times 10^{-7} > 7.1 \times 10^{-9}$, precipitation of PbI_2 will occur in this solution.

To determine the solubility-product constant for a sparingly soluble sub-stance, you need to determine the concentration of only one of the ions because the concentration of the other ion is related to the first ion's concen-tration by a simple stoichiometric relationship. Any method that accurately determines the concentration would be suitable. In this experiment, you will determine the solubility-product constant for Ag_2CrO_4. This substance con-tains the yellow chromate ion, CrO_4^{2-}. You will determine the concentration of the chromate ion spectrophotometrically at 375 nm.

Although the eye can discern differences in color intensity with reasonable accuracy, an instrument known as a *spectrophotometer*, which eliminates "human" limitations, is commonly used for this purpose. Basically, it is an instrument that measures the ratio I/I_0 where I is the intensity of light trans-mitted by a sample and I is the intensity of the incident beam. A schematic representation of a spectrophotometer is shown in Figure 8.1. The instrument has these five fundamental components:

- A light source that produces light with a wavelength range from about 375 to 650 nm if a visible range instrument only.

- A monochromator, which *selects* a particular wavelength of light and sends it to the sample cell with an intensity of I_0.

- The sample cell, which contains the solution being analyzed.

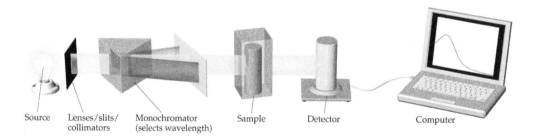

| Source | Lenses/slits/ collimators | Monochromator (selects wavelength) | Sample | Detector | Computer |

▲**FIGURE 8.1** Schematic representation of a spectrophotometer.

- A detector that measures the intensity, I, of the light transmitted from the sample cell; if the intensity of the incident light is I_0 and the solution absorbs light, the intensity of the transmitted light, I, is less than I_0.
- A display that indicates the intensity of the transmitted light.

For a given substance, the amount of light absorbed depends on the following:

- Concentration and identity of the absorbing species
- Cell or path length
- Wavelength of light
- Solvent

Plots of the amount of light absorbed versus wavelength are called *absorption spectra*. There are two common ways of expressing the amount of light absorbed. One is in terms of *percent transmittance*, *%T*, which is defined as

$$\%T = \frac{I}{I_0} \times 100\% \qquad [5]$$

As the term implies, percent transmittance corresponds to the percentage of light transmitted. When the sample in the cell is a solution, I is the intensity of light transmitted by the solution and I_0 is the intensity of light transmitted when the cell contains only solvent. Another method of expressing the amount of light absorbed is in terms of *absorbance*, A, which is defined by

$$A = \log \frac{I_0}{I} \qquad [6]$$

If a sample absorbs no light at a given wavelength, the percent transmittance is 100 and the absorbance is 0. On the other hand, if the sample absorbs all of the light, $\%T = 0$ and $A = \infty$. A is more useful in quantitative work since it varies linearly with concentration.

Absorbance is related to concentration by the Beer-Lambert law

$$A = abc$$

where A is absorbance, b is solution path length, c is concentration in moles per liter, and a is molar absorptivity or molar extinction coefficient. There is a linear relationship between absorbance and concentration when the Beer-Lambert law

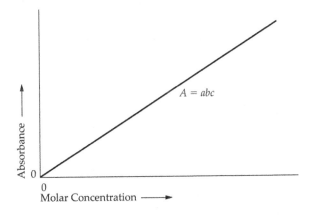

▲**FIGURE 8.2** Relationship between absorbance and molar concentration according to the Beer-Lambert law.

is obeyed, as illustrated in Figure 8.2. However, because deviations from this law occasionally occur, it is wise to construct a calibration curve of absorbance versus concentration.

PROCEDURE | A. Preparation of a Calibration Curve

WORK IN GROUPS OF FOUR TO OBTAIN YOUR CALIBRATION CURVE, BUT EVALUATE YOUR DATA INDIVIDUALLY. Using a buret, add 1, 5, 10, and 15 mL of standardized 0.0024 M K_2CrO_4 to each of four clean 100 mL volumetric flasks and dilute to the 100 mL mark with 0.25 M $NaNO_3$. Calculate the CrO_4^{2-} concentration in each solution. Measure the absorbance of these solutions at 375 nm and plot the absorbance versus concentration to construct your calibration curve as shown in Figure 8.2.

Operating Instructions for Spectronic 20

You may use a different spectrophotometer. If so, your instructor will explain how to use it.

1. Turn the wavelength control knob (Figure 8.3) to the desired wavelength.
2. Turn on the instrument by rotating the power control clockwise and allow the instrument to warm up about 5 min. With no sample in the holder but with the cover closed, turn the zero adjust to bring the meter needle to zero on the percent transmittance scale.
3. Fill the cuvette about halfway with distilled water (or solvent blank) and insert it in the sample holder, aligning the line on the cuvette with that of the sample holder. Close the cover and rotate the light control knob until the meter reads 100% transmittance.
4. Remove the blank from the sample holder and replace it with the cuvette containing the sample whose absorbance is to be measured. Align the lines on the cuvette with the holder and close the cover. Read the percent transmittance or optical density from the meter.

PROCEDURE | B. Determination of the Solubility-Product Constant

Accurately prepare three solutions in separate 150 mm test tubes by adding 5.00 mL of 0.0040 M $AgNO_3$ to 5.00 mL of 0.0024 M K_2CrO_4.

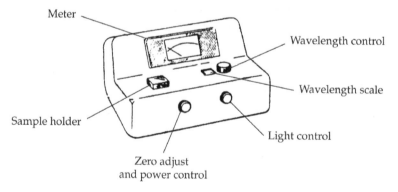

▲**FIGURE 8.3** Spectrophotometer controls.

Waste Disposal Instructions Because chromates are hazardous, you must treat all chromate solutions with care. Avoid spilling or touching these solutions. All excess K_2CrO_4 solution from Part A should be returned to a specially marked waste container, not to the original stock solution. All chromate solutions from Part B of the experiment should be placed in the same waste container. Likewise, all of the Ag_2CrO_4 samples should be disposed of in the second specially marked waste container. Silver nitrate ($AgNO_3$) solution is also hazardous. Any $AgNO_3$ solution that is spilled on the skin will cause discoloration after a few minutes, which can be avoided by immediately and thoroughly washing the affected area. All excess $AgNO_3$ solution should be returned to a third specially marked container. The other solution used in this experiment, $NaNO_3$, should be disposed of as indicated by your instructor.

GIVE IT SOME THOUGHT

a. Calculate the reaction quotient, Q, when these two solutions are mixed.

b. If a solid forms, what does that tell you about the value of Q versus K_{sp} ?

c. If a solid forms, what happens to the concentration of CrO_4^{2-} ?

Mix by rapping the solutions with your fingers to generate a vortex as in Appendix J. Perform this at periodic intervals for about 15 min to establish equilibrium between the solid phase and the ions in solution. Transfer approximately 3 mL of each solution along with most of the insoluble Ag_2CrO_4 to 75 mm test tubes and centrifuge. Discard the supernatant liquid and retain the precipitate as directed. To each of the test tubes add 2 mL of 0.25 M $NaNO_3$. Mix each test tube thoroughly and centrifuge again. Discard the supernatant liquid; then add 2 mL of 0.25 M $NaNO_3$ to each of the test tubes, mixing them vigorously and periodically for about 15 min to establish an equilibrium between the solid and the solution. Some solid Ag_2CrO_4 must remain in the test tubes. If none remains, start over. After mixing the test tubes for about 15 min, centrifuge the mixtures. Transfer the clear, pale yellow supernatant liquid from each of the three test tubes to a clean, dry cuvette. Measure and record the absorbance of the three solutions. Using your calibration curve, calculate the molar concentration of CrO_4^{2-} in each solution.

GIVE IT SOME THOUGHT

a. Why is $NaNO_3$ an appropriate choice for this solution?

b. Why can't you use NaCl?

c. Why is it necessary to have solid Ag_2CrO_4 present in the test tubes?

Note on Calculations

You are determining the K_{sp} of Ag_2CrO_4 in this experiment. The equilibrium reaction for the dissolution of Ag_2CrO_4 is

$$Ag_2CrO_4(s) \rightleftharpoons 2Ag^+(aq) + CrO_4^{2-}(aq)$$

for which $K_{sp} = [Ag^+]^2[CrO_4^{2-}]$.

You should note that at equilibrium, $[Ag^+] = 2[CrO_4^{2-}]$; hence, having determined the concentration of chromate ions, you know the silver ion concentration.

Name _____ Desk _____

Date _____ Laboratory Instructor _____

| Determination of the Solubility-Product Constant for a Sparingly Soluble Salt | 8 | Pre-lab Questions |

Before beginning this experiment in the laboratory, you should be able to answer the following questions.

1. Write the solubility equilibrium and the solubility-product constant expression for the slightly soluble salt CaF_2.

2. Calculate the number of moles of Ag^+ in 5.00 mL of 0.0040 M $AgNO_3$ and the number of moles of CrO_4^{2-} in 5.00 mL of 0.0024 M K_2CrO_4.

3. If 5 mL of 0.0040 M $AgNO_3$ is added to 5 mL of 0.0024 M K_2CrO_4, is either Ag^+ or CrO_4^{2-} in stoichiometric excess? If so, which one?

4. The K_{sp} for $BaCrO_4$ is 1.2×10^{-10}. Will $BaCrO_4$ precipitate when 10 mL of 1.0×10^{-5} M $Ba(NO_3)_2$ is mixed with 10 mL of 1.0×10^{-3} M K_2CrO_4?

5. The K_{sp} for $BaCO_3$ is 5.1×10^{-9}. How many grams of $BaCO_3$ will dissolve in 1000 mL of water?

6. Distinguish between the equilibrium constant expression and K_{sp} for the dissolution of a sparingly soluble salt.

7. List as many experimental techniques as you can that may be used to determine K_{sp} for a sparingly soluble salt.

8. Why must some solid remain in contact with a solution of a sparingly soluble salt in order to ensure equilibrium?

9. In general, when will a sparingly soluble salt precipitate from solution?

Name _____ Desk _____

Date _____ Laboratory Instructor _____

Determination of the Solubility-Product Constant for a Sparingly Soluble Salt

A. Preparation of a Calibration Curve

Initial $[CrO_4^{2-}]$ _____

Volume of 0.0024 M K_2CrO_4	Total volume	$[CrO_4^{2-}]$	Absorbance
1. _____	_____	_____	_____
2. _____	_____	_____	_____
3. _____	_____	_____	_____
4. _____	_____	_____	_____

Molar extinction coefficient for $[CrO_4^{2-}]$

1._____   2._____   3._____   4._____

Average molar extinction coefficient _____

Standard deviation (show calculations) _____

B. Determination of the Solubility-Product Constant

	Absorbance	$[CrO_4^{2-}]$	$[Ag^+]$	K_{sp} of Ag_2CrO_4
1.	_____	_____	_____	_____
2.	_____	_____	_____	_____
3.	_____	_____	_____	_____

Average K_{sp} (show calculations) _____

Standard deviation _____
(show calculations)

QUESTIONS

1. If the standard solutions had unknowingly been made up to be 0.0024 M AgNO$_3$ and 0.0040 M K$_2$CrO$_4$, would this have affected your results? If so, how?

2. If your cuvette had been dirty, how would this have affected the calculated value of K_{sp}?

3. Using your determined value of K_{sp}, calculate how many milligrams of Ag$_2$CrO$_4$ will dissolve in 10.0 mL of H$_2$O.

4. The experimental procedure for this experiment has you add 5 mL of 0.0040 M AgNO$_3$ to 5 mL of 0.0024 M K$_2$CrO$_4$. Is either of these reagents in excess? If so, which one?

5. Use your experimentally determined value of K_{sp} and show, by calculation, that Ag_2CrO_4 should precipitate when 5 mL of 0.0040 M $AgNO_3$ are added to 5 mL of 0.0024 M K_2CrO_4.

6. In the back of your textbook, look up the accepted value of K_{sp} for Ag_2CrO_4. Calculate the percentage error in your experimentally determined value for K_{sp}.

7. Although Ag_2CrO_4 is insoluble in water, it is soluble in dilute HNO_3. Explain using chemical equations.

8. What is the greatest source of error in this experiment?

9. Reviewing the procedure, indicate where careless work could contribute to the error source you identified in question 8.

Calibration curve

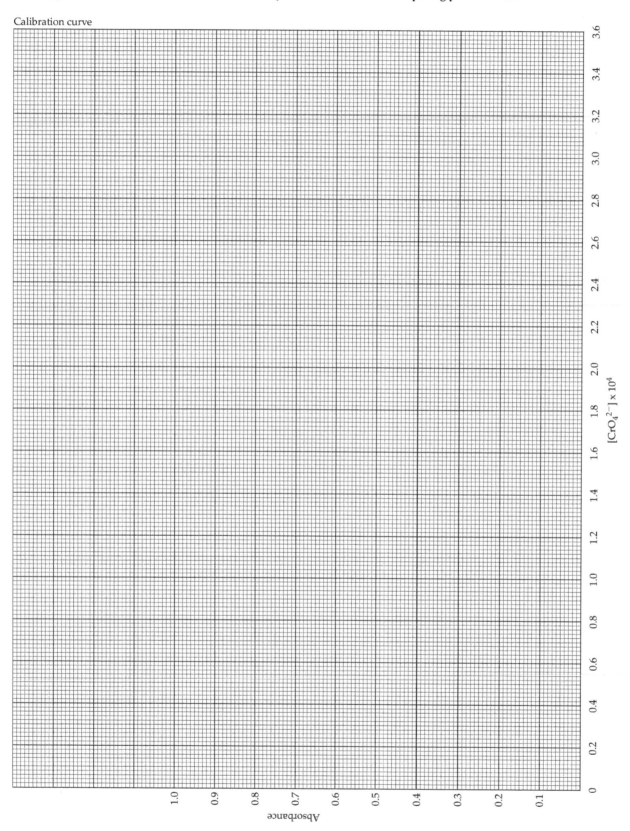

$[CrO_4^{2-}] \times 10^4$

Absorbance

Electrochemical Cells and Thermodynamics

9

To become familiar with some fundamentals of electrochemistry, including the Nernst equation, by constructing electrochemical (voltaic) cells and measuring their potentials at various temperatures. The quantities ΔG, ΔH, and ΔS are calculated from the temperature variation of the measured emf.

OBJECTIVE

Apparatus

DC voltmeter or potentiometer (to measure mV)	alligator clips and lead wires (2 sets)
emery cloth	50 mL test tubes (3)
600 mL beaker	glass U-tubes (to fit large test tubes) (3)
thermometer	
glass stirring rods (3)	cotton
Bunsen burner and hose clamps (2)	ring stand, two iron rings, and wire gauze
	test tube clamps (2)

APPARATUS AND CHEMICALS

Chemicals

1 M Pb(NO$_3$)$_2$	1 M Cu(NO$_3$)$_2$
1 M SnCl$_2$	0.1 M KNO$_3$
lead, tin, and copper strips or wire	ice
	agar

BACKGROUND

DISCUSSION

Electrochemistry is that area of chemistry that deals with the relations between chemical changes and electrical energy. It is primarily concerned with oxidation-reduction phenomena. Chemical reactions can be used to produce electrical energy in cells that are referred to as *voltaic*, or galvanic, cells (🔗Section 5.3). Electrical energy, on the other hand, can be used to bring about chemical changes in what are termed *electrolytic* cells (🔗Section 5.9). In this experiment, you will investigate some of the properties of voltaic cells.

In principle, any spontaneous redox reaction can be used to produce electrical energy. This task can be accomplished by means of a voltaic cell, a device in which electron transfer takes place through an external circuit or pathway rather than directly between reactants. One such spontaneous reaction occurs when a strip of zinc is immersed in a solution containing Cu^{2+}. As the reaction proceeds, the blue color of the $Cu^{2+}(aq)$ ions begins to fade and metallic copper deposits on the zinc strip. At the same time, the zinc begins to dissolve. The redox reaction that occurs is given in Equation [1].

$$Zn(s) + Cu^{2+}(aq) \longrightarrow Zn^{2+}(aq) + Cu(s) \qquad [1]$$

Figure 9.1 shows a voltaic cell that utilizes the same reaction. The two solid metal strips connected by the external circuit are called electrodes (✐ Figure 5.5). The electrode at which oxidation occurs is called the *anode*, and the electrode at which reduction occurs is called the *cathode*. The voltaic cell may be regarded as two "half-cells," one corresponding to the oxidation half-reaction and the other to the reduction half-reaction. Recall that a substance that loses electrons is said to be oxidized and a substance that gains electrons is said to be reduced. In the example below, Zn is oxidized and Cu^{2+} is reduced.

Anode (oxidation half-reaction) $Zn(s) \longrightarrow Zn^{2+}(aq) + 2e^-$

Cathode (oxidation half-reaction) $Cu^{2+}(aq) + 2e^- \longrightarrow Cu(s)$

Because Zn^{2+} ions are formed in one compartment and Cu^{2+} ions are depleted in the other compartment, a salt bridge is used to maintain electrical neutrality by allowing the migration of ions between these compartments.

The cell voltage, or electromotive force (*emf*), is indicated on the voltmeter in units of volts. The cell emf is also called the cell potential. The magnitude of the emf is a quantitative measure of the driving force or thermodynamic tendency for the reaction to occur. In general, the emf of a voltaic cell depends on the substances that make up the cell as well as on their concentration and temperature. Hence, it is a common practice to compare *standard cell potentials*, symbolized by $E°_{cell}$ (✐ Section 5.4). These potentials correspond to cell voltages under standard conditions: gases at 1 atm pressure; solutions at 1 *M* concentration and at 25 °C. For the Zn/Cu voltaic cell in Figure 9.1, the standard cell potential at 25 °C is 1.10 V.

$$Zn(s) + Cu^{2+}(aq, 1\,M) \longrightarrow Zn^{2+}(aq, 1\,M) + Cu(s) \qquad E°_{cell} = 1.10\ \text{V}$$

Recall that the superscript ° denotes standard state conditions (✐ Section 5.4).

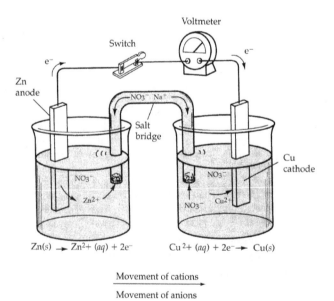

▲**FIGURE 9.1** A complete and functioning voltaic cell using a salt bridge to complete the electrical circuit.

The cell potential is the difference between two electrode potentials, one associated with the cathode and the other associated with the anode. By convention, the potential associated with each electrode is chosen to be the potential for reduction to occur at that electrode. Thus, standard electrode potentials are tabulated for reduction reactions, and they are denoted by the symbol, E_{red}°. The cell potential is given by the standard reduction potential of the cathode reaction, E_{red}° (cathode), *minus* the standard reduction potential of the anode reaction, E_{red}° (anode) as follows:

$$E_{cell}^\circ = E_{red}^\circ \text{ (cathode)} - E_{red}^\circ \text{(anode)} \qquad [2]$$

Because it is not possible to directly measure the potential of an isolated half-cell reaction, the standard hydrogen reduction half-reaction, in which $H^+(aq)$ is reduced to $H_2(g)$ under standard conditions, has been selected as a reference ($\mathscr{O}$ Section 5.4). It has been assigned a standard reduction potential of exactly 0 V.

$$2H^+(aq, 1\,M) + 2e^- \longrightarrow H_2(g, 1\,atm) \qquad E_{red}^\circ = 0 \text{ V}$$

An electrode designed to produce this half-reaction is called the standard hydrogen electrode (SHE). Figure 9.2 shows a voltaic cell using a SHE and a standard Zn^{2+}/Zn electrode. The spontaneous reaction occurring in this cell is the oxidation of Zn and the reduction of H^+.

$$Zn(s) + 2H^+(aq) \longrightarrow Zn^{2+}(aq) + H_2(g)$$

The standard cell potential for this cell is 0.76 V. By using the defined standard reduction potential of H^+ ($E_{red}^\circ = 0$ V) and Equation [2], you can determine the standard reduction potential for the Zn^{2+}/Zn half-reaction as follows:

$$E_{cell}^\circ = E_{red}^\circ \text{(cathode)} - E_{red}^\circ \text{(anode)}$$

$$0.76 \text{ V} = 0 \text{ V} - E_{red}^\circ \text{(anode)}$$

$$E_{red}^\circ \text{(anode)} = -0.76 \text{ V}$$

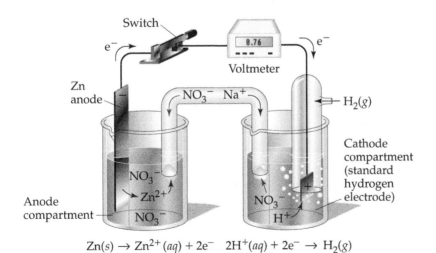

$$Zn(s) \rightarrow Zn^{2+}(aq) + 2e^- \quad 2H^+(aq) + 2e^- \rightarrow H_2(g)$$

▲**FIGURE 9.2** Voltaic cell using a standard hydrogen electrode.

Thus, a standard reduction potential of -0.76 V can be assigned to the reduction of Zn^{2+} to Zn as follows:

$$Zn^{2+}(aq, \ 1 \ M) + 2e^- \longrightarrow Zn(s) \qquad E^\circ_{red} = -0.76 \ V$$

Notice that the reaction is written as a reduction even though it is "running in reverse" as an oxidation in the cell in Figure 9.2. Whenever you assign a potential to a half-cell reaction, you write the reaction as a reduction reaction.

Standard reduction potentials for other half-reactions can be established in a manner similar to that used for the $Zn^{2+} \mid Zn$ half-reaction. The table in Appendix H lists some standard reduction potentials. Example 9.1 illustrates how this method can be used to determine the standard reduction potential for the $Cu^{2+} \mid Cu$ half-reaction.

EXAMPLE 9.1

The cell in Figure 9.1 may be represented by the following cell notation:

$$Zn \mid Zn^{2+}(aq) \parallel Cu^{2+}(aq) \mid Cu$$

The single bar represents the phase separation of the electrode from the solution. The double bar represents the salt bridge. The cell notation is generally written as | Anode || Cathode |. Given that E°_{cell} for this cell is 1.10 V, the Zn electrode is the anode, and the standard reduction potential of Zn^{2+} is –0.76 V, calculate the E°_{red} for the reduction of Cu^{2+} to Cu.

$$Cu^{2+}(aq, \ 1 \ M) + 2e^- \longrightarrow Cu(s)$$

SOLUTION: Use Equation [2] and the information provided. See Figure 9.3.

$$E^\circ_{cell} = E^\circ_{red}(cathode) - E^\circ_{red}(anode)$$

$$1.10 \ V = E^\circ_{red}(cathode) - (-0.76 \ V)$$

$$E^\circ_{red}(cathode) = 1.10 \ V - 0.76 \ V = 0.34 \ V$$

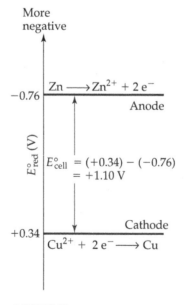

▲ **FIGURE 9.3** Half-cell potentials and standard cell potential for the Zn-Cu voltaic cell.

The free-energy change, ΔG, associated with a chemical reaction is a measure of the driving force or spontaneity of the process. If the free-energy change of a process is negative, the reaction will occur spontaneously in the direction indicated by the chemical equation (☞Section 5.5).

The cell potential of a redox process is related to the free-energy change as follows:

$$\Delta G = -nFE \qquad [3]$$

In this equation, F is Faraday's constant, the electrical charge on 1 mol of electrons is

$$1F = 96,485\frac{C}{\text{mol e}^-} = 96,485\frac{J}{\text{V-mol e}^-}$$

and n represents the number of moles of electrons transferred in the reaction. When both reactants and products are in their standard states, Equation [3] takes the following form:

$$\Delta G° = -nFE° \qquad [4]$$

EXAMPLE 9.2

Calculate the standard free-energy change associated with the redox reaction $2Ce^{4+} + Tl^+ \longrightarrow 2Ce^{3+} + Tl^{3+}$ ($E° = 0.450$ V). Would this reaction occur spontaneously under standard conditions?

SOLUTION:

$$\Delta G° = -nFE°$$

$$= -(2 \text{ mol e}^-)\left(\frac{96,485 \text{ J}}{\text{V-mol e}^-}\right)(0.450 \text{ V})$$

$$= -86.9 \times 10^3 \text{ J}$$

$$= -86.9 \text{ kJ}$$

Because $\Delta G° < 0$, this reaction would occur spontaneously.

The standard free-energy change of a chemical reaction is also related to the equilibrium constant for the reaction as follows:

$$\Delta G° = -RT \ln K \qquad [5]$$

where R is the gas law constant (8.314 J/K-mol) and T is the temperature in Kelvin. Consequently, $E°$ is also related to the equilibrium constant. From Equations [4] and [5], it follows that

$$-nFE° = -RT \ln K$$

$$E° = \frac{RT}{nF}\ln K \qquad [6]$$

When $T = 298$ K, $\ln K$ is converted to $\log K$, and the appropriate values of R and F are substituted, Equation [6] becomes

$$E° = \frac{0.0592}{n}\log K \qquad [7]$$

You can see from this relation that the larger K is, the larger the standard cell potential will be.

In practice, most voltaic cells are not likely to be operating under standard state conditions. It is possible, however, to calculate the cell emf, E, under non-standard state conditions with a knowledge of $E°$, temperature, and concentrations of reactants and products as follows:

$$E = E° - \frac{0.0592}{n} \log Q \qquad [8]$$

Q is called the reaction quotient; it has the form of an equilibrium constant expression, but the concentrations used to calculate Q are not equilibrium concentrations. The relationship given in Equation [8] is referred to as the Nernst equation (see Example 9.3) (⌀ Section 5.6).

Now consider the operation of the cell shown in Figure 9.1 in more detail. Earlier you saw that the reaction

$$Cu(aq)^{2+} + Zn(s) \longrightarrow Zn(aq)^{2+} + Cu(s)$$

is spontaneous. Consequently, it has a positive electrochemical potential ($E° = 1.10$ V) and a negative free energy ($\Delta G° = -nFE°$). As this reaction occurs, Cu^{2+} will be reduced and deposited as copper metal onto the copper electrode. The electrode at which reduction occurs is called the cathode. Simultaneously, zinc metal from the zinc electrode will be oxidized and go into solution as Zn^{2+}. The electrode at which oxidation occurs is called the anode. Effectively, then, electrons will flow in the external wire from the zinc electrode through the voltmeter to the copper electrode and be given up to copper ions in solution. These copper ions will be reduced to copper metal and plate out on the copper electrode. Concurrently, zinc metal will give up electrons to become Zn^{2+} ions in solution. These Zn^{2+} ions will diffuse through the salt bridge into the copper solution and replace the Cu^{2+} ions that are being removed. See Figure 9.4.

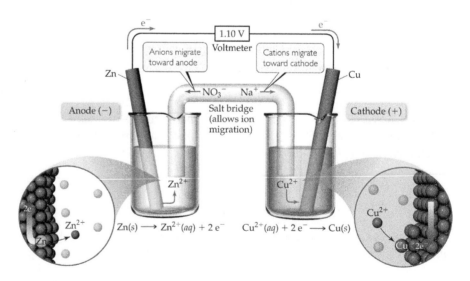

▲**FIGURE 9.4** Voltaic cell indicating movement of electrons and ions.

EXAMPLE 9.3

Calculate the cell potential for the cell

$$Zn \,|\, Zn^{2+}(0.60\ M) \,\|\, Cu^{2+}(0.20\ M) \,|\, Cu$$

given the following:

$$Cu(aq)^{2+} + Zn(s) \longrightarrow Cu(s) + Zn(aq)^{2+} \qquad E° = 1.10\ V$$

(HINT: Recall that Q includes expressions for species in solution but not for pure solids.)

SOLUTION:

$$
\begin{aligned}
E &= E° - \frac{0.0592}{n}\log\frac{[Zn^{2+}]}{[Cu^{2+}]} \\
&= 1.10\ V - \frac{0.0592}{2}\log\frac{[0.60]}{[0.20]} \\
&= 1.10 - 0.014 \\
&= 1.086 \\
&= 1.09\ V
\end{aligned}
$$

You can see that changes in concentrations have small effects on the cell emf because of the log term in the above equation.

A list of the properties of electrochemical cells and some definitions of related terms are given in Table 9.1.

Chemists have developed a shorthand notation for electrochemical cells, as shown in Example 9.1. The notation for the Cu-Zn cell that explicitly shows concentrations is as follows:

$$Zn \,|\, Zn^{2+}(xM) \,\|\, Cu^{2+}(yM) \,|\, Cu$$

Anode	Cathode
(oxidation)	(reduction)

In this notation, the anode (oxidation half-cell) is written on the left and the cathode (reduction half-cell) is written on the right.

Your objective in this experiment is to construct a set of three electrochemical cells and to measure their cell potentials. With a knowledge of two half-cell potentials and the cell potentials obtained from your measurements, you will calculate the other half-cell potentials and the equilibrium constants for the reactions. By measuring the cell potential as a function of temperature, you may also determine the thermodynamic constants, ΔG, ΔH, and ΔS, for the reactions. This can be done with the aid of Equation [9].

$$\Delta G = \Delta H - T\Delta S \qquad\qquad [9]$$

ΔG may be obtained directly from measurements of the cell potential using the following relationship:

$$\Delta G = -nFE$$

TABLE 9.1 Summary of Properties of Electrochemical Cells and Some Definitions

Voltaic cells: $E > 0$, $\Delta G < 0$; reaction spontaneous, K large (greater than 1)
Electrolytic cells: $E < 0$, $\Delta G > 0$; reaction nonspontaneous, K small (less than 1)
Anode: electrode at which oxidation occurs
Cathode: electrode at which reduction occurs
Oxidizing agent: species accepting electrons to become reduced
Reducing agent: species donating electrons to become oxidized

A plot of ΔG versus temperature in Kelvin will give $-\Delta S$ as the slope and ΔH as the intercept. A more accurate measure of ΔH can be obtained, however, by substituting ΔG and ΔS back into Equation [9] and calculating ΔH.

EXAMPLE 9.4

For the voltaic cell

$$Pb \,|\, Pb^{2+}(1\ M) \,\|\, Cu^{2+}(1\ M) \,|\, Cu$$

the following data were obtained:

$E = 0.464$ V	$T = 298$ K
$E = 0.468$ V	$T = 308$ K
$E = 0.473$ V	$T = 318$ K

Calculate ΔG, ΔH, and ΔS for this cell.

SOLUTION:

$$\Delta G = -nFE$$

At 298 K,

$$\Delta G = -(2\ \text{mol e}^-)(96{,}485\ \text{J/V-mol e}^-)(0.464\ \text{V})(1\ \text{kJ}/1000\ \text{J})$$
$$= -89.5\ \text{kJ}$$

At 308 K,

$$\Delta G = -(2\ \text{mol e}^-)(96{,}485\ \text{J/V-mol e}^-)(0.468\ \text{V})(1\ \text{kJ}/1000\ \text{J})$$
$$= -90.3\ \text{kJ}$$

At 318 K,

$$\Delta G = -(2\ \text{mol e}^-)(96{,}485\ \text{J/V-mol e}^-)(0.473\ \text{V})(1\ \text{kJ}/1000\ \text{J})$$
$$= -91.3\ \text{kJ}$$

Because $\Delta G = \Delta H - T\Delta S$, a plot of ΔG versus T in Kelvin gives $\Delta H = -64.2$ kJ/mol and $\Delta S = 85.0$ J/mol-K.

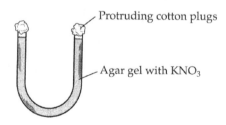

Protruding cotton plugs

Agar gel with KNO_3

▲**FIGURE 9.5** U-tube salt bridge.

Before setting up pairs of half-cells, make a complete cell of the type shown in Figure 9.1 in the following manner illustrated in Figure 9.6: Place 30 mL of $1\,M$ $Pb(NO_3)_2$ and 30 mL of $1\,M$ $Cu(NO_3)_2$ in separate large test tubes. Obtain a lead strip and a copper strip and clean the surfaces of each with emery cloth or sandpaper. Boil 100 mL of $0.1\,M$ KNO_3. Remove this solution from the heat and add to the boiling solution 1 g of agar, stirring constantly until all of the agar dissolves. Invert a U-tube and fill the U-tube with this solution before it cools, leaving about a half inch of air space at each end of the U-tube as shown in Figure 9.5. The cotton plugs must protrude from the ends of the U-tube. Construct two additional agar-filled U-tubes in the same manner. Place a U-tube in the test tubes as a salt bridge, as shown in Figure 9.6.

Insert the lead strip into the $Pb(NO_3)_2$ solution and the copper strip into the $Cu(NO_3)_2$ solution. Obtain a voltmeter and attach the positive lead to the copper strip and the negative lead to the lead strip using alligator clips. Read the voltage. Check that the alligator clips make good contact with the metal strips. Record this voltage and the temperature of the cells on your report sheet. If your measured potential is negative, reverse the wire connection. Now construct the following cells and measure their voltages in the same manner.

$$Sn\,|\,Sn^{2+}(1\,M)\,\|\,Cu^{2+}(1\,M)\,|\,Cu$$

$$Pb\,|\,Pb^{2+}(1\,M)\,\|\,Sn^{2+}(1\,M)\,|\,Sn$$

PROCEDURE

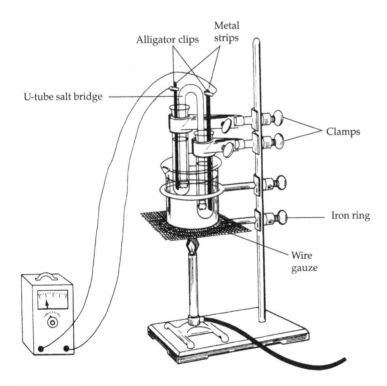

▲**FIGURE 9.6** Electrochemical reaction apparatus.

GIVE IT SOME THOUGHT

a. In the cells you constructed, which half-reaction occurs at the anode?
b. Which half reaction occurs at the cathode?
c. Explain your choice.
d. In each of these cells, do you observe a spontaneous reaction?
e. How can you observe this experimentally?

GIVE IT SOME THOUGHT

Consider the cell illustrated in Figure 9.4

a. Do the concentrations of $Cu^{2+}(aq)$ and $Zn^{2+}(aq)$ increase, decrease, or remain the same as the reaction proceeds?
b. Does the mass of the $Cu(s)$ and $Zn(s)$ increase, decrease, or remain the same as the reaction proceeds?
c. Why do the concentrations and masses change?

Record the voltage and temperature of each cell on your report sheet. From the measured voltages, calculate the half-cell potentials for the lead and tin half-cells and the equilibrium constants for these two reactions. In these calculations, use $E° = 0.34$ V for the $Cu^{2+} \mid Cu$ couple.

GIVE IT SOME THOUGHT

Describe a voltaic cell consistent with Figure 9.1 by sketching each voltaic cell. In your sketch, label the anode and cathode compartments and indicate the half-reaction occurring at the anode and the cathode, the overall cell reaction, the overall cell potential, the direction of electron flow, and the ions present in the anode and cathode compartments.

Now choose any one of the three cells and measure the cell potential as a function of temperature as follows: Insert the metal strips into each of two 50 mL test tubes containing the respective 1 M cation solution and place the test tubes in a 600 mL beaker containing about 200 mL of distilled water.

Place the U-tube into the two test tubes and connect the metallic strips to the voltmeter as before (see Figure 9.6). Because the voltage changes are of the order of 30 mV for the temperature range you will study, make certain the voltmeter you use is sensitive enough to detect these small changes.

Begin heating the water in the 600 mL beaker, using your Bunsen burner. Make sure the test tubes are clamped firmly in place. *Do not move* any part of the cell; if you do, the voltage will fluctuate. Heat the cell to approximately 70 °C. Measure the temperature and record it on your report sheet. Determine the cell potential at this temperature and record it on your report sheet. Remove the Bunsen burner and record the temperature and voltage at 15° intervals as the cell cools to room temperature. Finally, replace the beaker of water with a beaker containing an ice-water mixture, being careful not to move the test tubes and their contents. After the cell has been in the ice-water mixture for about 10 min, measure the temperature of the ice-water mixture in the 600 mL beaker and record it and the cell potential. You have determined the cell potential at various temperatures. Calculate ΔG for the cell at each of these temperatures and plot ΔG versus temperature on the graph paper provided. The slope of the plot is $-\Delta S$. From the values of ΔG and ΔS, calculate ΔH at 298 K. If time permits, determine the temperature dependence of E for another cell.

GIVE IT SOME THOUGHT

a. Which variable would you plot on the x- and y-axis on your graph?

b. Rearrange Equation [9] $(\Delta G = \Delta H - T\Delta S)$ into $y = mx + b$.
Which of the following graphs should yours resemble?

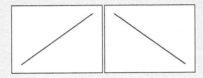

Dispose of the solutions in the test tubes and the agar containing U-tubes in the designated waste container.

NOTES AND CALCULATIONS

Electrochemical Cells and Thermodynamics | 9 | Pre-lab Questions

Before beginning this experiment in the laboratory, you should be able to answer the following questions.

1. Define the following terms: *faraday*, *salt bridge*, *anode*, *cathode*, *voltaic cell*, and *electrolytic cell*.

2. Write a chemical equation for the reaction that occurs in the following cell: $Cu \mid Cu^{2+}(aq) \parallel Ag^{+}(aq) \mid Ag$.

3. Given the following E's, calculate the standard-cell potential for the cell in question 2.

$$Cu^{2+}(aq) + 2e^{-} \longrightarrow Cu(s) \qquad E^{\circ} = +0.34 \text{ V}$$
$$Ag^{+}(aq) + e^{-} \longrightarrow Ag(s) \qquad E^{\circ} = +0.80 \text{ V}$$

4. Calculate the voltage of the following cell:

$$Zn \mid Zn^{2+}(0.10 \, M) \parallel Cu^{2+}(0.20 \, M) \mid Cu$$

5. Calculate the cell potential, the equilibrium constant, and the free-energy change for

$$Ca(s) + Mn^{2+}(aq)(1 \, M) \rightleftharpoons Ca^{2+}(aq)(1 \, M) + Mn(s)$$

given the following E° values:

$$Ca^{2+}(aq) + 2e^{-} \longrightarrow Ca(s) \qquad E^{\circ} = -2.87 \text{ V}$$
$$Mn^{2+}(aq) + 2e^{-} \longrightarrow Mn(s) \qquad E^{\circ} = -1.18 \text{ V}$$

6.   Would you normally expect $\Delta H°$ to be positive or negative for a voltaic cell? Justify your answer.

7.   Predict whether the following reactions are spontaneous.

$Pd(aq)^{2+} + H_2(g) \longrightarrow Pd(s) + 2H(aq)^+$ $Pd(aq)^{2+} + 2e^- \longrightarrow Pd(s)$
$$E° = 0.987 \text{ V}$$

$Sn(aq)^{4+} + H_2(g) \longrightarrow Sn(aq)^{2+} + 2H^+$ $Sn(aq)^{4+} + 2e^- \longrightarrow Sn(aq)^{2+}$
$$E° = 0.154 \text{ V}$$

$Ni(aq)^{2+} + H_2(g) \longrightarrow Ni(s) + 2H(aq)^+$ $Ni(aq)^{2+} + 2e^- \longrightarrow Ni(s)$
$$E° = -0.250 \text{ V}$$

$Cd(aq)^{2+} + H_2(g) \longrightarrow Cd(s) + 2H(aq)^+$ $Cd(aq)^{2+} + 2e^- \longrightarrow Cd(s)$
$$E° = -0.403 \text{ V}$$

From your answers, decide which of the above metals could be reduced by hydrogen.

8.   Identify the oxidizing agents and reducing agents in the reactions in question 7.

REPORT SHEET | EXPERIMENT

Electrochemical Cells and Thermodynamics | 9

Shorthand cell designation	Temperature (°C)	E cell (measured)	ΔG (calculated)	K_{eq} (calculated)
1. _____	_____	_____	_____	_____
2. _____	_____	_____	_____	_____
3. _____	_____	_____	_____	_____

Show calculations for $\Delta G°$ and K_{eq} for an exemplary pair. For $Pb \mid Pb^{2+} \parallel Sn^{2+} \mid Sn$:

Half-cell equation	E half-cell (calculated)
1. _____	_____
2. _____	_____
3. _____	_____

Effect of Temperature on Cell Potential

Cell designation: E (measured)	Temperature (°C)	Temperature (K)	ΔG (calculated)
_____	_____	_____	_____
_____	_____	_____	_____
_____	_____	_____	_____
_____	_____	_____	_____
_____	_____	_____	_____
_____	_____	_____	_____

ΔS determined from the slope of a plot of ΔG versus T _____

$\Delta H°$ calculated at 298 K _____ (show calculations)

Is the cell reaction endothermic or exothermic? _____

QUESTIONS

1. Write the net ionic equations that occur in the following cells:

   $Pb \mid Pb(NO_3)_2 \parallel AgNO_3 \mid Ag$

   $Zn \mid ZnCl_2 \parallel Pb(NO_3)_2 \mid Pb$

   $Pb \mid Pb(NO_3)_2 \parallel NiCl_2 \mid Ni$

2. Which of the following reactions will have the larger emf under standard conditions? Why?

   $$CuSO_4(aq) + Pb(s) \rightleftharpoons PbSO_4(s) + Cu(s)$$
   $$Cu(NO_3)_2(aq) + Pb(s) \rightleftharpoons Pb(NO_3)_2(aq) + Cu(s)$$

3. Calculate ΔG for the reaction in Example 9.3.

4. Voltages listed in textbooks and handbooks are given as *standard cell potentials* (voltages). What is meant by a standard cell? Were the cells constructed in this experiment standard cells? Why or why not?

5. As a standard voltaic cell runs, it "discharges" and the cell potential decreases with time. Explain.

6. Using standard potentials given in the appendices, calculate the standard cell potentials and the equilibrium constants for the following reactions:

   $$Cu(s) + 2Ag^+(aq) \rightleftharpoons Cu^{2+}(aq) + 2Ag(s)$$
   $$Zn(s) + Fe^{2+}(aq) \rightleftharpoons Zn^{2+}(aq) + Fe(s)$$

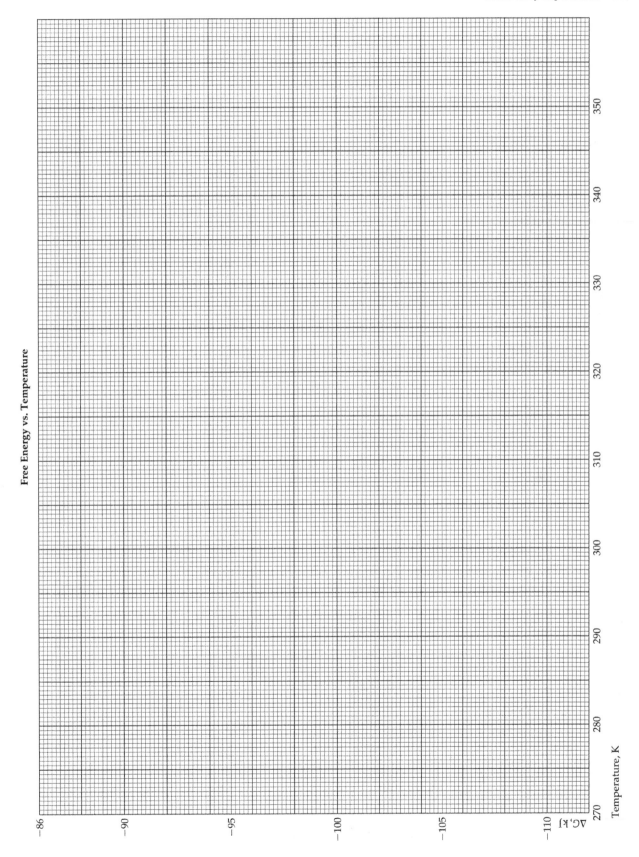

Free Energy vs. Temperature

$\Delta G, kJ$

Temperature, K

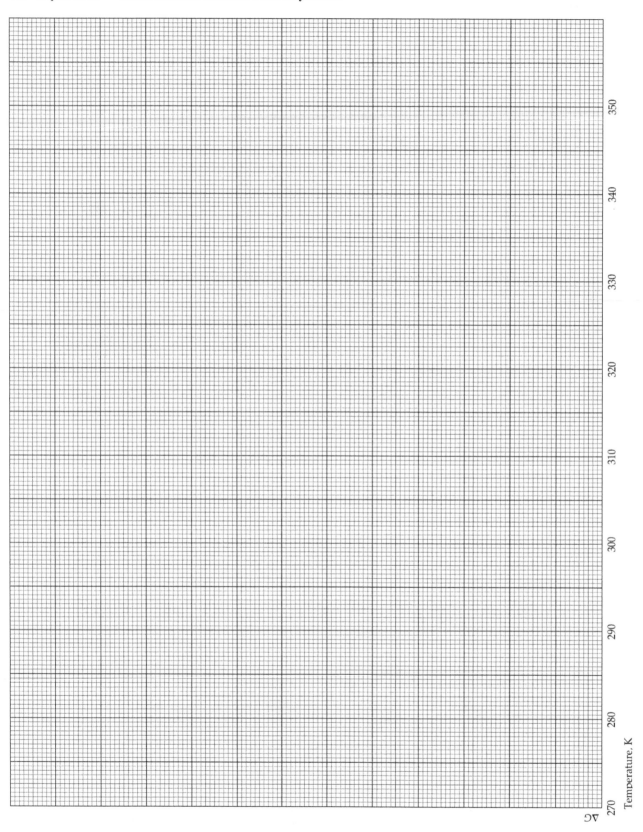

Temperature. K

ΔG

Preparation and Reactions of Coordination Compounds: Oxalate Complexes

10

To gain familiarity with coordination compounds by preparing a representative compound and witnessing some typical reactions.

OBJECTIVE

Apparatus

APPARATUS AND CHEMICALS

balance	9 cm Büchner funnel
Bunsen burner and hose or hotplate	250 mL suction flask
	aspirator
8 oz wide-mouth bottle	100 and 250 mL beakers
No. 6 two-hole rubber stopper	thermometer
glass stirring rod	ring stand and iron ring
9 cm filter paper	glass wool
wire gauze	
vial	

Chemicals

cis- and *trans*-$K[Cr(C_2O_4)_2(H_2O)_2]$ (prep given)	aluminum powder
	$6\ M$ KOH
$6\ M$ NH_3	$H_2C_2O_4$ (oxalic acid)
$K_2C_2O_4 \cdot H_2O$ (potassium oxalate monohydrate)	$K_2Cr_2O_7$ (potassium dichromate)
	50% ethanol
acetone	95% ethanol
ferrous ammonium sulfate	absolute ethanol
$6\ M$ H_2SO_4	$CuSO_4 \cdot 5(H_2O)$
ice	6% H_2O_2
	$6\ M$ HCl

When gaseous boron trifluoride, BF_3, is passed into liquid trimethylamine, $(CH_3)_3 N$, a highly exothermic reaction occurs and a creamy white solid, $(CH_3)_3 N: BF_3$, separates. This solid, which is an adduct of trimethylamine and boron trifluoride, is a coordination compound. It contains a coordinate covalent, or dative, bond that unites the Lewis acid BF_3 with the Lewis base trimethylamine. Numerous coordination compounds are known; in fact, nearly all compounds of the transition elements are coordination compounds wherein the metal is a Lewis acid and the atoms or molecules joined to the metal are Lewis bases. These Lewis bases are called *ligands*, and the coordination

DISCUSSION

compounds are usuallydenoted by square brackets when their formulas are written ($\mathscr{P}$ Section 4.2). The metal and the ligands bound to it constitute what is termed the coordination sphere. When writing chemical formulas for coordination compounds, you use square brackets to set off the coordination sphere from other parts of the compound. For example, the salt $NiCl_2 \cdot 6H_2O$ is, in reality, the coordination compound $[Ni(H_2O)_6]Cl_2$, with an octahedral geometry, as shown in Figure 10.1.

 ## GIVE IT SOME THOUGHT

What is the coordination number of nickel in this complex?

The apexes of a *regular* octahedron are all equivalent positions ($\mathscr{P}$ Section 4.2). Thus, each of the monodentate (one donor site or Lewis base electron pair) H_2O molecules in the $[Ni(H_2O)_6]^{2+}$ ion and the three bidentate (two donor sites) oxalate ions, $C_2O_4^{2-}$, in $[Co(C_2O_4)_3]^{2-}$ are in identical environments. The water molecules in the two isomeric compounds, *cis-* and *trans-*$[Cr(C_2O_4)_2(H_2O)_2]^-$, are in equivalent environments within each complex ion (coordination compound), but the two isomeric ions are not equivalent to each other. The two water molecules are adjacent in the *cis* isomer and opposite each other in the *trans* isomer. These two isomers are termed *geometric isomers* ($\mathscr{P}$ Section 4.3), and although they have identical empirical and molecular formulas, their geometrical arrangements in space are different ($\mathscr{P}$ Section 4.4).

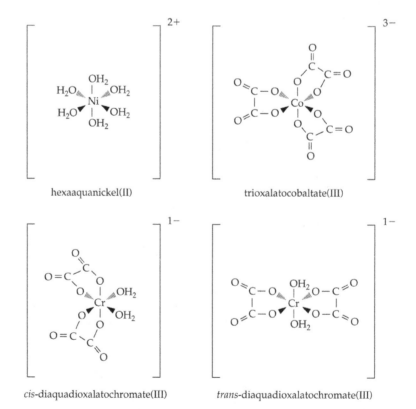

hexaaquanickel(II)   trioxalatocobaltate(III)

cis-diaquadioxalatochromate(III)   *trans*-diaquadioxalatochromate(III)

▲**FIGURE 10.1** Typical octahedral (6-coordinate) coordination compounds.

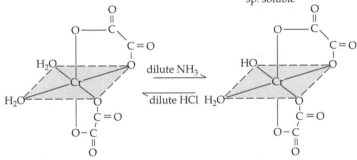

trans isomer (rose-violet)

hydroxo complex (light brown)
sp. soluble

cis isomer (purple-green) dichroic

hydroxo complex (deep green)
very soluble

▲**FIGURE 10.2** Reaction of geometric isomers: *cis*- and *trans*-$[Cr(C_2O_4)_2(H_2O)_2]^-$ ions. The procedure is to place a small amount of an aqueous solution of each complex on separate pieces of filter paper on a watch glass. Let them dry; then add a drop of reagent. Observe the results.

Consequently, they have different chemical and physical properties, as your laboratory instructor will demonstrate through the reactions shown in Figure 10.2.

Your goal in this experiment is to prepare an oxalate-containing coordination compound. It may be analyzed for its oxalate concentration by the procedure described in Experiment 37. You will prepare *one* of the following compounds:

- $K_3[Cr(C_2O_4)_3] \cdot 3H_2O$
- $K_2[Cu(C_2O_4)_2] \cdot 2H_2O$
- $K_3[Fe(C_2O_4)_3] \cdot 3H_2O$
- $K_3[Al(C_2O_4)_3] \cdot 3H_2O$

Your laboratory instructor will tell you which one to prepare. Someone in your lab section will prepare each of these compounds so that you can compare their properties. (**CAUTION:** *Oxalic acid is a toxic compound and is absorbed through the skin. Should any come in contact with your skin, wash it off immediately with copious amounts of water.*)

Prepare one of the complexes whose synthesis is given below.

PROCEDURE

1. Preparation of $K_3[Cr(C_2O_4)_3] \cdot 3H_2O$

$$K_2Cr_2O_7 + 7H_2C_2O_4 \cdot 2H_2O + 2K_2C_2O_4 \cdot H_2O \longrightarrow$$
$$2K_3[Cr(C_2O_4)_3] \cdot 3H_2O + 6CO_2 + 17H_2O$$

GIVE IT SOME THOUGHT

What is the coordination number of chromium in the $K_3[Cr(C_2O_4)_3] \cdot 3H_2O$ complex?

In the hood, slowly add 3.6 g of potassium dichromate to a suspension of 10 g of oxalic acid in 20 mL of H_2O in a 250 mL beaker. The orange-colored mixture should spontaneously warm up almost to boiling as a vigorous evolution of gas commences. When the reaction has subsided (about 15 min), dissolve 4.2 g of potassium oxalate monohydrate in the hot green-black liquid and heat to boiling for 10 min. Allow the beaker and its contents to cool to room temperature. Add about 10 mL of 95% ethanol, with stirring, into the cooled solution in the beaker. Further cool the beaker and its contents in ice. The cooled liquid should thicken with crystals. After cooling the liquid in ice for 15 to 20 min, collect the crystals by filtration with suction using a Büchner funnel (See Figure 10.3) and filter flask. Wash the crystals on the funnel with three 10 mL portions of 50% aqueous ethanol followed by 25 mL of 95% ethanol and dry the product in air. Determine the mass of the air-dried material and store it in a vial. You should obtain about 9 g of product. Calculate the theoretical yield and determine your percentage yield. Reactions of chromium(III) are slow, and your yield will be low if you work too fast.

$$\% \text{ yield} = \frac{\text{actual yield in grams}}{\text{theoretical yield in grams}} \times 100\%$$

Your instructor may tell you to save your sample for analysis in Experiment 37 or dispose of it as directed.

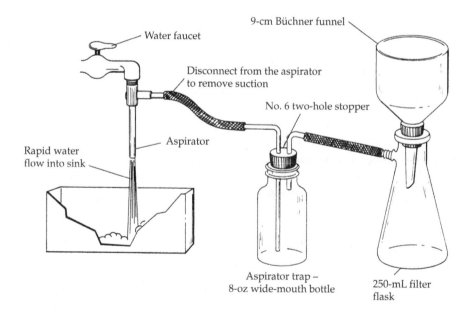

▲**FIGURE 10.3** Suction filtration assembly.

EXAMPLE 10.1

In the preparation of *cis*-$K[Cr(C_2O_4)_2(H_2O)_2] \cdot 2H_2O$, 12.0 g of oxalic acid was allowed to react with 4.00 g of potassium dichromate and 8.20 g of *cis*-$K[Cr(C_2O_4)_2(H_2O)_2] \cdot 2H_2O$ was isolated. What is the percent yield in this synthesis?

SOLUTION:

$$K_2Cr_2O_7 + 7H_2C_2O_4 \cdot 2H_2O \longrightarrow 2K[Cr(C_2O_4)_2(H_2O)_2] \cdot 2H_2O$$
$$+ 6CO_2 + 13H_2O$$

From the above reaction, you can see that 1 mol of $K_2Cr_2O_7$ reacts with 7 mol of $H_2C_2O_4$ to produce 2 mol of $K[Cr(C_2O_4)_2(H_2O)_2] \cdot 2H_2O$. In the synthesis, you used the following:

$$\text{moles } K_2Cr_2O_7 = \frac{4.00 \text{ g}}{294.19 \text{ g/mol}} = 0.0136 \text{ mol}$$

$$\text{moles } H_2C_2O_4 \cdot 2H_2O = \frac{12.0 \text{ g}}{126.07 \text{ g/mol}} = 0.0952 \text{ mol}$$

The reaction requires a 7:1 molar ratio of oxalic acid to $K_2Cr_2O_7$, but you actually used a 6.999 molar ratio (or within experimental error, the stoichiometric amount of each reagent and there is no limiting reagent). Hence, the number of moles of $K[Cr(C_2O_4)_2(H_2O)_2] \cdot 2H_2O$ formed should be twice the number of moles of $K_2Cr_2O_7$ or 2/7 of the moles of oxalic acid reacted.

$$\text{moles } K[Cr(C_2O_4)_2(H_2O)_2] \cdot 2H_2O(\text{expected}) = (2)(0.0136 \text{ mol}) = 0.0272 \text{ mol}$$

The theoretical yield of $K[Cr(C_2O_4)_2(H_2O)_2] \cdot 2H_2O$ is

$$(0.0272 \text{ mol})(339.2 \text{ g/mol}) = 9.23 \text{ g}$$

The percentage yield is then

$$\% \text{ yield} = \frac{(8.20 \text{ g})}{(9.23 \text{ g})}(100\%) = 88.8\%$$

2. Preparation of $K_2[Cu(C_2O_4)_2] \cdot 2H_2O$

$$CuSO_4 \cdot 5H_2O + 2K_2C_2O_4 \cdot H_2O \longrightarrow K_2[Cu(C_2O_4)_2] \cdot 2H_2O$$
$$+ K_2SO_4 + 5H_2O$$

Heat a solution of 6.2 g of copper sulfate pentahydrate in 12 mL of water to about 90 °C and add it rapidly, while stirring vigorously, to a hot (~90 °C) solution of 10.0 g of potassium oxalate monohydrate ($K_2C_2O_4 \cdot H_2O$) in 50 mL of water contained in a 100 mL beaker. Cool the mixture by setting the beaker in an ice bath for 15 to 30 min. Suction-filter the resultant crystals using a Büchner funnel (see Figure 10.3) and filter flask. Wash the crystals successively with about 12 mL of cold water, then 10 mL of absolute ethanol, and finally 10 mL of acetone and air-dry. Determine the mass of the air-dried material and store it in a vial. You should obtain about 7 g of product. Calculate the theoretical yield and determine your percentage yield. Your instructor may tell you to save your sample for analysis in Experiment 37 or dispose of it as directed. **(CAUTION: *Keep ethanol away from flames.*)**

3. Preparation of $K_3[Fe(C_2O_4)_3] \cdot 3H_2O$

$$Fe(NH_4)_2(SO_4)_2 \cdot 6H_2O + H_2C_2O_4 \cdot 2H_2O \longrightarrow$$

$$FeC_2O_4 + H_2SO_4 + (NH_4)_2SO_4 + 8H_2O$$

$$H_2C_2O_4 \cdot 2H_2O + 2FeC_2O_4 + 3K_2C_2O_4 \cdot H_2O + H_2O_2 \longrightarrow$$

$$2K_3[Fe(C_2O_4)_3] \cdot 3H_2O + H_2O$$

This preparation contains two separate parts. Iron(II) oxalate is prepared first and then converted to $K_3[Fe(C_2O_4)_3] \cdot 3H_2O$ by oxidation with hydrogen peroxide, H_2O_2, in the presence of potassium oxalate.

Prepare a solution of 10 g of ferrous ammonium sulfate hexahydrate in 30 mL of water containing a few drops of $6M$ H_2SO_4 (to prevent premature oxidation of Fe^{2+} to Fe^{3+} by O_2 in the air). Then add, while stirring, a solution of 6 g of oxalic acid in 50 mL of H_2O. Yellow iron(II) oxalate forms. Carefully heat the mixture to boiling while stirring constantly to prevent bumping. Decant and discard the supernatant liquid as directed and wash the precipitate several times by adding about 30 mL of hot water, stirring, and decanting the liquid. Filtration is not necessary at this point.

To the wet iron(II) oxalate, add a solution of 6.6 g of $K_2C_2O_4 \cdot H_2O$ in 18 mL of water and heat the mixture to about 40 °C. *Slowly and cautiously* add 17 mL of 6% H_2O_2 while stirring constantly and maintaining the temperature at 40 °C. After the addition of H_2O_2 is complete, heat the mixture to boiling and add a solution containing 1.7 g of oxalic acid in 15 mL of water. When adding the oxalic acid solution, add the first 8 mL all at once and the remaining 5 mL dropwise, keeping the temperature near boiling. Remove any solid by gravity filtration and add 20 mL of 95% ethanol to the filtrate. Cover the beaker with a watch glass and store it in your lab desk until the next laboratory period. Filter by suction using a Büchner funnel and filter flask (Figure 10.3) and wash the green crystals with a 50% aqueous ethanol solution, then with acetone, and air-dry. Determine the mass of the product and store it in a vial in the dark. This complex is photosensitive and reacts with light as follows:

$$[Fe(C_2O_4)_3]^{3-} \xrightarrow{\ hv\ } [Fe(C_2O_4)_2]^{2-} + 2CO_2 + e^-$$

GIVE IT SOME THOUGHT

What is the purpose of adding the hydrogen peroxide in this step?

To demonstrate this, place a small specimen on a watch glass near the window and observe any changes that occur during the lab period. You should obtain about 8 g of product. Calculate the theoretical yield and determine your percent yield. Your instructor may tell you to save your sample for analysis in Experiment 37 or dispose of it as directed. Keep it away from light by wrapping the vial with aluminium foil.

4. Preparation of $K_3[Al(C_2O_4)_3]\cdot 3H_2O$

$$Al + 3KOH + 3H_2C_2O_4\cdot 2H_2O \longrightarrow K_3[Al(C_2O_4)_3]\cdot 3H_2O + 6H_2O + \tfrac{3}{2}H_2$$

Place 1 g of aluminum powder in a 200 mL beaker and cover with 10 mL of hot water. Add 20 mL of 6 *M* KOH solution in small portions to regulate the vigorous evolution of hydrogen. Finally, heat the liquid almost to boiling on a hot plate to dissolve any residual metal. Maintain the heating and in small portions, add a solution of 13 g of oxalic acid in 100 mL of water. During the neutralization, hydrated alumina will precipitate, but it will redissolve at the end of the addition after gentle boiling. Cool the solution in an ice bath and add 50 mL of 95% ethanol. If oily material separates, stir the solution and scratch the sides of the beaker with your glass rod to induce crystallization. Suction-filter the product using the Büchner funnel (see Figure 10.3) and suction flask and wash with a 20 mL portion of ice-cold 50% aqueous ethanol and then with small portions of absolute ethanol. Air-dry the product, determine its mass and store it in a stoppered bottle. You should obtain about 11 g of product. Calculate the theoretical yield and determine your percent yield. Your instructor may tell you to save your sample for analysis in Experiment 37 or dispose of as directed.

Preparation of Materials for the Demonstration

(These preparations should be done a week before the laboratory period.)

cis- $K[Cr(C_2O_4)_2(H_2O)_2]\cdot 2H_2O$

$$K_2Cr_2O_7 + 7H_2C_2O_4\cdot 2H_2O \rightleftharpoons$$
$$2K[Cr(C_2O_4)_2(H_2O)_2]\cdot 2H_2O + 6CO_2 + 13H_2O$$

In a hood, separately powder in a *dry* mortar 12 g of oxalic acid dihydrate and 4 g of potassium dichromate. Mix the powders as intimately as by grinding gently in the mortar. Moisten a large evaporating dish (10 cm) with water and pour off all of the water but do not wipe dry. Place the powdered mixture in the evaporating dish as a *compact heap*; it will become moistened by the water that remains in the evaporating dish. Cover the evaporating dish with a large watch glass and warm it gently on a hot plate. A vigorous spontaneous reaction will soon occur and will be accompanied by frothing as steam and CO_2 escape. The mixture should then liquefy to a deep-colored syrup. Pour about 20 mL of 95% ethanol on the hot liquid and continue to warm it gently on the hot plate. Triturate (grind or crush) the product with a spatula until it solidifies. If you cannot effect complete solidification with one portion of 95% alcohol, decant the liquid, add another 20 mL of 95% alcohol, warm gently, and resume the trituration until the product is entirely crystalline and granular. The yield is essentially quantitative at about 9 g. This compound is intensely dichroic (appears different colors when viewed from different directions or lighting conditions), appearing in the solid state as almost black in diffuse daylight and deep purple in artificial light.

trans- $K[Cr(C_2O_4)_2(H_2O)_2]\cdot 3H_2O$

Dissolve 12 g of oxalic acid dihydrate in a minimum of boiling water in a 300 mL (or larger) beaker. In a hood, add to this in small portions a solution of 4 g of potassium dichromate in a minimum of hot water and cover the beaker with a watch glass while the violent reaction proceeds. After the addition is complete, cool the contents of the beaker and allow spontaneous evaporation at room temperature to occur so that the solution reduces to about one-third its original volume (this takes 36 to 48 hours). Collect the deposited crystals by suction filtration, wash several times with cold water and 95% alcohol, and air-dry. The yield is about 6.5 g. The complex is rose-colored with a violet tinge and is not dichroic.

 GIVE IT SOME THOUGHT

What are the differences in the physical properties of the cis and trans isomers?

Waste Disposal Instructions All oxalate- metal-containing solutions, and ethanol containing solutions should be disposed of in appropriate waste containers.

Preparation and Reactions of Coordination Compounds: Oxalate Complexes

10 Pre-lab Questions

Before beginning this experiment in the laboratory, you should be able to answer the following questions.

1. Define the terms *Lewis acid* and *Lewis base*.

2. Define the terms *ligand* and *coordination sphere*.

3. Define and give an example of a coordination compound.

4. Define the term *geometric isomer*.

5. Draw structures for all possible isomers of the six-coordinate compounds $[Co(NH_3)_4Cl_2]$ and $[Co(NH_3)_3Cl_3]$.

6. Are the chlorine atoms in equivalent environments in each of the compounds $[Co(NH_3)_4Cl_2]$ and $[Co(NH_3)_3Cl_3]$?

7.   What is the meaning of *dichroism*?

8.   What is the meaning of *trituration*?

9.   Look up the preparation of an oxalate complex of Ni, Mn, or Co. Cite your reference and state whether this preparation would be suitable to add to this experiment. Explain.

10.   Find an analytical method to determine the amount of Fe, Cu, Cr, or Al in your oxalate complex. Cite the reference to the method. Could you determine the amount using the chemicals and equipment available in your laboratory? Why or why not?

11.   Oxalic acid is used to remove rust and corrosion from automobile radiators. How do you think it works?

Name _____ Desk _____

Date _____ Laboratory Instructor _____

Preparation and Reactions of Coordination Compounds: Oxalate Complexes

1. Complex prepared _____

2. Chemical reaction for its preparation

3. Theoretical yield of oxalate complex (show calculations):

4. Experimental yield of oxalate complex _____

5. Percent yield of oxalate complex (show calculations):

6. Color and general appearance of complex:

7. Describe the reactions of *cis*- and *trans*-$K[Cr(C_2O_4)_2(H_2O)_2]$ with NH_3 and the reverse reactions with HCl using chemical equations. List any observations, such as color changes and apparent solubilities.

8. Is your complex soluble in H_2O ? _____   Alcohol? _____   Acetone? _____

QUESTIONS

1. Sodium trioxalatocobaltate(III) trihydrate is prepared by the following reactions:

$$[Co(H_2O)_6]Cl_2 + K_2C_2O_4 \cdot H_2O \longrightarrow CoC_2O_4 + 2KCl + 7H_2O$$

$$2CoC_2O_4 + 4H_2O + H_2O_2 + 4Na_2C_2O_4 \longrightarrow 2Na_3[Co(C_2O_4)_3] \cdot 3H_2O + 2NaOH$$

What is the percent yield of $Na_3[Co(C_2O_4)_3] \cdot 3H_2O$ if 7.6 g is obtained from 12.5 g of $[Co(H_2O)_6]Cl_2$?

2. Why are $K_3[Cr(C_2O_4)_3] \cdot 3H_2O$, $K_2[Cu(C_2O_4)_2] \cdot 2H_2O$ and $K_3[Fe(C_2O_4)_3] \cdot 3H_2O$ colored, whereas $K_3[Al(C_2O_4)_3] \cdot 3H_2O$ is colorless?

3. What are the names of the following compounds?

   a. $K_3[Cr(C_2O_4)_3] \cdot 3H_2O$

   b. $K_2[Cu(C_2O_4)_2] \cdot 2H_2O$

   c. $K_3[Fe(C_2O_4)_3] \cdot 3H_2O$

   d. $K_3[Al(C_2O_4)_3] \cdot 3H_2O$

4. What is the percent oxalate in each of the following compounds?

   a. $K_3[Cr(C_2O_4)_3] \cdot 3H_2O$

   b. $K_2[Cu(C_2O_4)_2] \cdot 2H_2O$

   c. $K_3[Fe(C_2O_4)_3] \cdot 3H_2O$

   d. $K_3[Al(C_2O_4)_3] \cdot 3H_2O$

Alcohols and Phenols | 11

LABORATORY GOALS

- Describe the chemical and physical properties of alcohols and phenols.
- Classify an alcohol as primary, secondary, or tertiary.
- Perform a chemical test to distinguish between the classes of alcohols.
- Draw the condensed structural formulas of the oxidation products of alcohols.

LAB INFORMATION

Time: 2 h

Caution: ***Be careful when you work with chromate solution. It contains concentrated acid. Do not use burners in lab when you work with flammable organic compounds.***
Tear out the lab report sheets and place them beside the matching procedures.

Related Topics: Alcohols, classification of alcohols, solubility of alcohols in water, phenols, oxidation of alcohols

Dispose of all chemicals as directed by your lab instructor.

CHEMICAL CONCEPTS

A. Structures of Alcohols and Phenol

Alcohols are organic compounds that contain the hydroxyl group ($\sim$ OH). The simplest alcohol is methanol. Ethanol is found in alcoholic beverages and preservatives and is used as a solvent. 2-Propanol, also known as rubbing alcohol or isopropyl alcohol, is found in astringents and perfumes.

$$CH_3—OH$$

Methanol
(methyl alcohol)

$$CH_3—CH_2—OH$$

Ethanol
(ethyl alcohol)

$$CH_3—\overset{\displaystyle OH}{\underset{|}{CH}}—CH_3$$

2-Propanol
(isopropyl alcohol)

Hand sanitizers are used to kill bacteria and viruses that spread colds and flu. As a gel or liquid solution, many hand sanitizers use ethanol as their active ingredient. The amount of ethanol in an alcohol-containing sanitizer is typically 60% (v/v), but can be as high as 85% (v/v). The high volume of ethanol can make hand sanitizers a fire hazard in the home because ethanol is highly flammable. When using an ethanol-containing sanitizer, it is important to rub your hands until they are completely dry. It is also recommended that sanitizers containing ethanol be stored in areas away from heat sources in the home.

▲ Hand sanitizers that contain ethanol are used to kill bacteria on the hands.

A benzene ring with a hydroxyl group is known as phenol. Concentrated solutions of phenol are caustic and cause burns. However, derivatives of phenol, such as thymol, are used as antiseptics and are sometimes found in cough drops.

Phenol

Thymol
(2-isopropyl-5-methylphenol)

Classification of Alcohols

In a primary (1°) alcohol, the carbon atom attached to the —OH group is bonded to one other carbon atom. In a secondary (2°) alcohol, the carbon with the —OH is attached to two carbon atoms, and in a tertiary (3°) alcohol it is attached to three carbon atoms.

Ethanol
primary (1°) alcohol

2-Propanol
secondary (2°) alcohol

2-Methyl-2-Propanol
tertiary (3°) alcohol

B. Properties of Alcohols and Phenol

The polarity of the hydroxyl group (—OH) makes alcohols with one to three carbon atoms completely soluble with water because they can form many hydrogen bonds. An alcohol with four carbon atoms is somewhat soluble, whereas the large hydrocarbon portion in longer chain alcohols makes them insoluble in water.

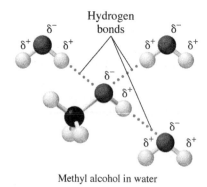

Methyl alcohol in water

▲ Hydrogen bonds form between the hydroxyl group and H and O atoms in water.

Acidity of Phenol

In water, phenol acts as a weak acid because the hydroxyl group ionizes slightly. Although phenol has six carbon atoms, the polarity of the hydroxyl group makes it soluble in water.

| Phenol | | Phenoxide ion |

C. Oxidation of Alcohols

Primary and secondary alcohols are easily oxidized. An oxidation consists of removing an H from the —OH group and another H from the C atom attached to the —OH group. Tertiary alcohols do not undergo oxidation because there are no H atoms on that C atom attached to the —OH. Primary and secondary alcohols can be distinguished from tertiary alcohols using a solution with chromate, CrO_4^{2-}. When an oxidation has occurred, the orange color of the chromate solution turns green.

D. Iron(III) Chloride Test

Phenols react with the Fe^{3+} ion in iron(III) chloride ($FeCl_3$) solution to give complex ions with strong colors from red to purple.

Phenol   + Fe^{3+} ⟶ Fe^{3+} (phenol complex)
Colorless   *Yellow*   *Purple*

E. Identification of an Unknown

The group of tests for alcohols and phenols described in this experiment will be used to identify the functional group and family of an unknown.

EXPERIMENTAL PROCEDURES   *GOGGLES REQUIRED!*

A. Structures of Alcohols and Phenol

Materials: Display of models: ethanol, 2-propanol, and 2-methyl-2-propanol

Draw the condensed structural formula of each model in the display and for phenol. Classify each as a primary, secondary, or tertiary alcohol.

B. Properties of Alcohols and Phenol

Materials: 6 test tubes, pH paper, stirring rod, ethanol, 2-propanol, 2-methyl-2-propanol (*t*-butyl alcohol), cyclohexanol, 20% phenol, and unknown, ***Caution: Avoid contact with phenol.***

pH

1.   Place 10 drops of ethanol, 2-propanol, *t*-butyl alcohol (2-methyl-2-propanol), cyclohexanol, 20% phenol, and the unknown into six separate test tubes. Obtain some pH paper. Use a stirring rod to place a drop of each on a piece of pH paper. Clean the stirring rod between applications. Compare the color of the pH paper with the color chart on the container to determine the pH. Record your observations. Save the test tubes and alcohols for part **2**.

Solubility in water

2.   Add 2 mL of water (40 drops) to each test tube. Shake and determine the solubility in water of each alcohol. If the compound is soluble in water, you will see a clear solution with no separate layers. If it is insoluble, a cloudy mixture or separate layer will form. Record your observations.

DISPOSE OF ORGANIC COMPOUNDS IN DESIGNATED WASTE CONTAINERS!

C. Oxidation of Alcohols

Materials: 6 test tubes, ethanol, 2-propanol, 2-methyl-2-propanol (*t*-butyl alcohol), cyclohexanol, 20% phenol, unknown, 2% chromate solution

1.   Place 8 drops of ethanol, 2-propanol, 2-methyl-2-propanol (*t*-butyl alcohol), cyclohexanol, 20% phenol, and the unknown into six separate test tubes. Carefully add 2 drops of chromate solution to each. Stir carefully to allow the alcohol to react. ***Caution: Chromate solution contains concentrated H_2SO_4, which is corrosive.*** Look for a color change in the chromate solution. If a test tube becomes hot, place it in a beaker of ice-cold water. Record your observation of the color after 2 minutes.
2.   Draw the condensed structural formula of each alcohol.
3.   Classify each alcohol as primary (1°), secondary (2°), or tertiary (3°).
4.   If the orange color turned green within 2 min, oxidation of the alcohol has taken place. If the color remained orange, no reaction has occurred.

     If a reaction occurred, draw the condensed structural formulas of the product. When there is no change in color, no oxidation took place. In this case, write "no reaction" (NR).

DISPOSE OF ORGANIC COMPOUNDS IN DESIGNATED WASTE CONTAINERS!

D. Iron(III) Chloride Test

Materials: 6 test tubes, ethanol, 2-propanol, 2-methyl-2-propanol (*t*-butyl alcohol), cyclohexanol, 20% phenol, unknown, 1% $FeCl_3$ solution

Place 5 drops of the alcohols and unknown in separate test tubes. Add 5 drops of 1% $FeCl_3$ solution to each. Stir and record observations.

DISPOSE OF ORGANIC COMPOUNDS IN DESIGNATED WASTE CONTAINERS!

E. Identification of an Unknown

Use the test results to identify your unknown as one of the five compounds used in this experiment. Draw the condensed structural formula of the unknown.

Date _____   Name _____

Section _____   Team _____

Instructor _____   _____

Pre-Lab Study Questions | 11

1. What is the functional group of an alcohol and a phenol?

2. Why are some alcohols soluble in water?

3. Classify each of the following alcohols as primary, secondary or tertiary.

   a. 3-pentanol   _____

   b. 2-methyl-2-butanol _____

   c. 1-propanol   _____

4. If you add chromate, an oxidizing agent, to each of the following, would a green Cr^{3+} solution be formed?

   a. 3-pentanol   _____

   b. 2-methyl-2-butanol _____

   c. 1-propanol   _____

5. If an alcohol solution has a pH of 5, would it be a primary alcohol, a secondary alcohol, a tertiary alcohol, or a phenol?

REPORT SHEET | LAB

Alcohols and Phenols | 11

A. Structures of Alcohols and Phenols

Ethanol	2-Propanol
Classification:	
2-methyl-2-propanol (*t*-butyl alcohol)	Phenol
Classification:	

Questions and Problems

Q1 Draw the condensed structural formula and give the classification for each of the following alcohols:

1-Pentanol	3-Pentanol
Classification:	
Cyclopentanol	1-Methylcyclopentanol
Classification:	

B. Properties of Alcohols and Phenols   Unknown # _____

Alcohol	1. pH	2. Soluble in Water?
Ethanol		
2-Propanol		
2-Methyl-2-propanol		
Cyclohexanol		
Phenol		
Unknown		

C. Oxidation of Alcohols

Alcohol	1. Color After 2 min	2. Condensed Structural Formula	3. Classification	4. Condensed Structural Formula of Oxidation Product
Ethanol				
2-Propanol				
2-Methyl-2-propanol				
Cyclohexanol				
Phenol				
Unknown				

Q2 Draw the condensed structural formula of the product of the following reactions (if no reaction, write NR):

a. $CH_3-CH_2-CH_2-OH \xrightarrow{[O]}$

b. $CH_3-\overset{\displaystyle OH}{\underset{\displaystyle |}{CH}}-CH_2-CH_3 \xrightarrow{[O]}$

c.

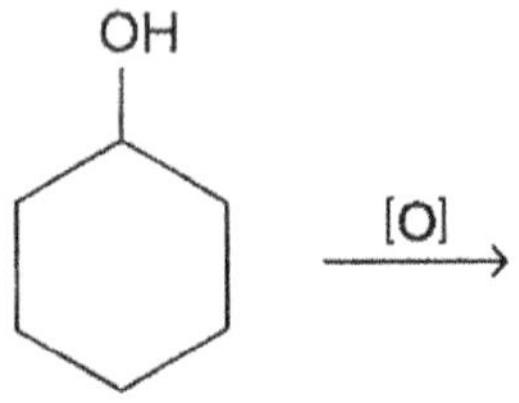

D. Iron(III) Chloride Test

Alcohol	FeCl$_3$ Test (Color)
Ethanol	
2-Propanol	
t-Butyl alcohol	
Cyclohexanol	
Phenol	
Unknown	

E. Identification of an Unknown

Unknown # _____

Summary of Testing	Test Results	Conclusions
B.1 pH		
B.2 Soluble in water?		
C.1 CrO_4^{2-}		
D $FeCl_3$		
Name of Unknown	**Condensed Structural Formula**	

Common Ions

Positive Ions (Cations)

1+
ammonium (NH_4^+)
cesium (Cs^+)
copper(I) or cuprous (Cu^+)
hydrogen (H^+)
lithium (Li^+)
potassium (K^+)
silver (Ag^+)
sodium (Na^+)

2+
barium (Ba^{2+})
cadmium (Cd^{2+})
calcium (Ca^{2+})
chromium(II) or chromous (Cr^{2+})
cobalt(II) or cobaltous (Co^{2+})
copper(II) or cupric (Cu^{2+})
iron(II) or ferrous (Fe^{2+})
lead(II) or plumbous (Pb^{2+})
magnesium (Mg^{2+})
manganese(II) or manganous (Mn^{2+})
mercury(I) or mercurous (Hg_2^{2+})

mercury(II) or mercuric (Hg^{2+})
strontium (Sr^{2+})
nickel(II) (Ni^{2+})
tin(II) or stannous (Sn^{2+})
zinc (Zn^{2+})

3+
aluminum (Al^{3+})
chromium(III) or chromic (Cr^{3+})
iron(III) or ferric (Fe^{3+})

Negative Ions (Anions)

1−
acetate (CH_3COO^- or $C_2H_3O_2^-$)
bromide (Br^-)
chlorate (ClO_3^-)
chloride (Cl^-)
cyanide (CN^-)
dihydrogen phosphate ($H_2PO_4^-$)
fluoride (F^-)
hydride (H^-)
hydrogen carbonate or
   bicarbonate (HCO_3^-)

hydrogen sulfite or bisulfite (HSO_3^-)
hydroxide (OH^-)
iodide (I^-)
nitrate (NO_3^-)
nitrite (NO_2^-)
perchlorate (ClO_4^-)
permanganate (MnO_4^-)
thiocyanate (SCN^-)

2−
carbonate (CO_3^{2-})
chromate (CrO_4^{2-})
dichromate ($Cr_2O_7^{2-}$)
hydrogen phosphate (HPO_4^{2-})
oxide (O^{2-})
peroxide (O_2^{2-})
sulfate (SO_4^{2-})
sulfide (S^{2-})
sulfite (SO_3^{2-})

3−
arsenate (AsO_4^{3-})
phosphate (PO_4^{3-})

Fundamental Constants*

Atomic mass constant	1 amu	$= 1.660539040 \times 10^{-27}$ kg
	1 g	$= 6.022140857 \times 10^{23}$ amu
Avogadro's number†	N_A	$= 6.022140857 \times 10^{23}$/mol
Boltzmann Constant	k	$= 1.3806485 \times 10^{-23}$ J/K
Electron charge	e	$= 1.6021766208 \times 10^{-19}$ C
Faraday constant	F	$= 9.648533289 \times 10^4$ C/mol
Gas constant	R	$= 0.0820582$ L-atm/mol-K
		$= 8.3144598$ J/mol-K
Mass of electron	m_e	$= 5.4857990946 \times 10^{-4}$ amu
		$= 9.10938356 \times 10^{-31}$ kg
Mass of neutron	m_n	$= 1.008664916$ amu
		$= 1.674927471 \times 10^{-27}$ kg
Mass of proton	m_p	$= 1.007276466$ amu
		$= 1.672621898 \times 10^{-27}$ kg
Pi	π	$= 3.1415926535$
Planck constant	h	$= 6.626070040 \times 10^{-34}$ J-s
Speed of light in vacuum	c	$= 2.99792458 \times 10^8$ m/s

*Fundamental constants are listed at the National Institute of Standards and Technology (NIST) Web site: http://physics.nist.gov/cuu/Constants/index.html

†Avogadro's number is also referred to as the Avogadro constant. The latter term is the name adopted by agencies such as the International Union of Pure and Applied Chemistry (IUPAC) and the National Institute of Standards and Technology (NIST), but "Avogadro's number" remains in widespread usage and is used in most places in this book.

Useful Conversion Factors and Relationships

Length

SI unit: meter (m)

$$1 \text{ km} = 0.62137 \text{ mi}$$
$$1 \text{ mi} = 5280 \text{ ft}$$
$$= 1.6093 \text{ km}$$
$$1 \text{ m} = 1.0936 \text{ yd}$$
$$1 \text{ in.} = 2.54 \text{ cm (exactly)}$$
$$1 \text{ cm} = 0.39370 \text{ in.}$$
$$1 \text{ Å} = 10^{-10} \text{ m}$$

Mass

SI unit: kilogram (kg)

$$1 \text{ kg} = 2.2046 \text{ lb}$$
$$1 \text{ lb} = 453.59 \text{ g}$$
$$= 16 \text{ oz}$$
$$1 \text{ amu} = 1.660538921 \times 10^{-27} \text{ kg}$$

Temperature

SI unit: Kelvin (K)

$$0 \text{ K} = -273.15 \text{ °C}$$
$$= -459.67 \text{ °F}$$
$$\text{K} = \text{°C} + 273.15$$
$$\text{°C} = \tfrac{5}{9}(\text{°F} - 32°)$$
$$\text{°F} = \tfrac{9}{5}\text{°C} + 32°$$

Energy (derived)

SI unit: Joule (J)

$$1 \text{ J} = 1 \text{ kg-m}^2/\text{s}^2$$
$$= 0.2390 \text{ cal}$$
$$= 1 \text{C-V}$$
$$1 \text{ cal} = 4.184 \text{ J}$$
$$1 \text{ eV} = 1.602 \times 10^{-19} \text{ J}$$

Pressure (derived)

SI unit: Pascal (Pa)

$$1 \text{ Pa} = 1 \text{ N/m}^2$$
$$= 1 \text{ kg/m-s}^2$$
$$1 \text{ atm} = 1.01325 \times 10^5 \text{ Pa}$$
$$= 760 \text{ torr}$$
$$= 14.70 \text{ lb/in}^2$$
$$1 \text{ bar} = 10^5 \text{ Pa}$$
$$1 \text{ torr} = 1 \text{ mm Hg}$$

Volume (derived)

SI unit: cubic meter (m³)

$$1 \text{ L} = 10^{-3} \text{ m}^3$$
$$= 1 \text{ dm}^3$$
$$= 10^3 \text{ cm}^3$$
$$= 1.0567 \text{ qt}$$
$$1 \text{ gal} = 4 \text{ qt}$$
$$= 3.7854 \text{ L}$$
$$1 \text{ cm}^3 = 1 \text{ mL}$$
$$1 \text{ in}^3 = 16.4 \text{ cm}^3$$

Color Chart for Common Elements

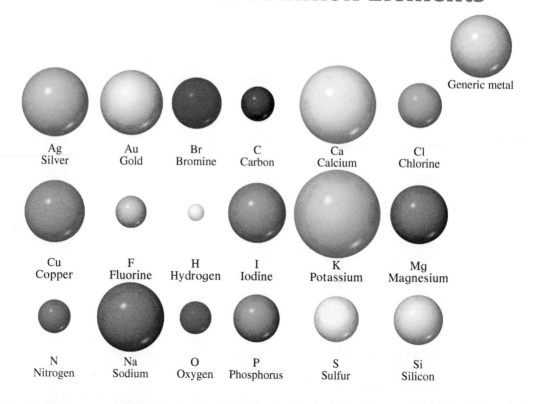

| Ag Silver | Au Gold | Br Bromine | C Carbon | Ca Calcium | Cl Chlorine |

Generic metal

| Cu Copper | F Fluorine | H Hydrogen | I Iodine | K Potassium | Mg Magnesium |

| N Nitrogen | Na Sodium | O Oxygen | P Phosphorus | S Sulfur | Si Silicon |